Brok

Mike Reiners
2004

Broken Vessels

The Spiritual Structure of Human Frailty

ELEVEN LECTURES
DORNACH, SWITZERLAND, SEPTEMBER 1924

by

RUDOLF STEINER

Foreword by

MICHAEL LIPSON, PH.D.

ANTHROPOSOPHIC PRESS

FOUNDATIONS OF
ANTHROPOSOPHICAL MEDICINE
VOLUME 7

For a complete listing of series see page 176

Published by Anthroposophic Press
P.O. Box 799
Great Barrington, MA 01230
www.steinerbooks.org

The eleven lectures presented here were given in Dornach from September 8
to September 18, 1924. In the collected edition of Rudolf Steiner's works,
the volume containing the German texts is entitled *Das Zusammenwirken
von Ärzten und Seelsorgen: Pastoral-Medizinischer Kurs* (vol. 318 in the Biblio-
graphic Survey).

The lectures in this volume, translated from the German by Gladys Hahn,
were previously published by Anthroposophic Press under the title *Pastoral
Medicine: The Collegial Working of Doctors and Priests* (1987).

Copyright © 1987, 2003 by Anthroposophic Press, Inc.

Library of Congress Cataloging-in-Publication Data

Steiner, Rudolf, 1861-1925.
[Zusammenwirken von Ärzten und Seelsorgern. English]
Broken vessels : the spiritual structure of human frailty : a series of lectures /
by Rudolf Steiner ; introduction by Michael Lipson ; [translated from the
German ... by Gladys Hahn].
p. cm.
ISBN 0-88010-503-8
1. Anthroposophy.
[DNLM: 1. Religion and Medicine.] I. Lipson, Michael, 1957- II.
Title.
BP595.S894 Z86513 2002
299'.935—dc21 2001002011

Book design by Studio 31
www.studio31.com

10 9 8 7 6 5 4 3 2 1

Printed in the United States of America

Contents

Foreword

Michael Lipson, Ph.D.

A man who lives by himself, scavenging from garbage in New York's Central Park, walks into my office having already been diagnosed as a schizophrenic by the previous psychologist who treated him. He says he wants psychotherapy, and I ask him what his concerns are. He first asks if he may clip his nails into my wastebasket, then pulls out some clippers from one of the many plastic bags that serve him as a portable apartment and proceeds to cut his nails (frighteningly deep into the quick) as he ponders how to put his case. Finally, musing over the wastebasket, he comes up with the key points of his problem.

"Well," he says as he surveys a newly bleeding fingertip, "Two things. First, I'm bothered by all this Muzak everywhere. You can't go into a public space anymore without hearing this junk. And second, I'm having a hard time understanding Shakespeare's play *The Tempest*. Can you help me?"

What kind of problem does this man really have? I agree with him that Muzak is pernicious and *The Tempest* demanding. Does he have an illness at all? The loose way he moves his limbs, the reekingly unwashed clothes he wears, the furtive glances he casts, and the abruptness of his responses — even if it were not for that self-harming behavior with the nail clippers — all suggest oddities of soul and body. In the actual encounter with such a person, labels like "schizophrenia," "manic depression," or "schizoaffective disorder" can seem painfully inadequate both to the depth of the problem and to the glimpsed *health* of some of his responses.

It becomes evident to caregivers, at least during our more honest moments, that we do not understand the immensity of the processes at work in this kind of condition. Not only our diagnostic labels, but the concepts behind them, can seem paltry in the face of intense psychic otherness. We can sense that both psychiatric drugs and standard psychotherapy are not adequate to the issues, even if they provide important relief at times.

In the eleven lectures that make up this volume, Rudolf Steiner attempts to reveal something about the invisible structure of health and illness as they are seen with the second sight of spiritual research. He delivered these talks at a time of furious activity — September of 1924 — during a month in which he offered a total of some seventy lectures on themes as various as dramatic arts and the Apocalypse of St. John. He also made room in that jam-packed schedule to receive over four hundred people for private consultations. It was a last, incandescent burst of generosity that many feel contributed to his death the following March.

This particular lecture course, formerly titled *Pastoral Medicine*, was given to a mixed audience of priests and physicians to show the interpenetration of medical and spiritual issues in caring for suffering humanity. While Steiner insists that the two professions should remain quite distinct, cooperating rather than merging, his exposition of the nature of human frailty occupies a middle ground of equal relevance to the priest and to the physician. This middle ground could be called psychology, except that it includes descriptions of spiritual principles, qualities, and entities that are as foreign to contemporary psychology as to medicine and theology. On the one hand, Steiner points out that "all processes in the human organism are spiritual"; on the other hand, "even the lobe of an ear can under certain conditions be clearly revealing of some psychological peculiarity," so that we can hardly keep these fields separate. He thus revives the ancient Greek understanding by which their word *psyche* meant both "soul" and "life of the body."

As in many of his talks, Steiner here throws out hints about the nature of this theme that are enormously suggestive but not fully elaborated, or are elaborated elsewhere. One such hint suggests the *developmental* aspect of the soul-body unity: "The forces that build the physical organism in the first seven years of human life are the same forces by which later we think." On such a view, what we normally conceive of as bodily and as mental are reenvisaged as facets of a single enormously complex, living process of incarnation whose components shift and interweave through time.

From the standpoint of promoting normal incarnation, Steiner takes up the developmental theme in those spiritual-scientific observations of child development that serve as the basis of Waldorf education (for example, in his *Education of the Child*). The current lecture cycle, by contrast, can be thought of as examining elements in this development as it occurs in adults who have *not* developed harmoniously. The lectures are, after all, addressed to those who work professionally with human brokenness. To meet inner frailty with truly adequate concepts (surely the necessary preamble to devising adequate therapies) Steiner must describe experiences that escape ordinary perception. In this lie both the promise and the pitfalls of what he has to offer.

We have a tendency nowadays, as spiritually inclined folk, to talk only in the vaguest terms about "hidden depths" of the soul. Steiner instead delineated specific inner structures in both healthy and unhealthy states. We have a related tendency, when we feel more materialistic, to ascribe spiritual experience to brain activity or even pathology — like those contemporary analysts who see Hildegard von Bingen and other visionaries as suffering from migraines. Steiner instead acknowledged such experience as real even if unbalanced from a certain standpoint. Thus in this book Steiner describes the extreme states of ecstasy achieved by the sixteenth-century Carmelite St. Teresa of Avila neither as merely pathological nor as exclusively healthy, but as a particular configuration of human inner structures.

The time has come to consider these "inner structures" more directly. Steiner talks not only about a physical but also about an "etheric" and an "astral" body, which can operate either more or less harmoniously and whose interconnections can be felicitous or dangerous. The terms he used were familiar to Steiner's anthroposophical audience, so that they needed no explanation during this lecture course. He had been writing and teaching about them for at least twenty years (see his discussions in *Theosophy*, published in 1904, and in *An Outline of Esoteric Science*, published in 1909). His audience in 1924 either knew what he meant or at least found itself on familiar ground when, for example, he said of certain mentally retarded persons that "the physical body remains comparatively isolated because the etheric body . . . does not entirely penetrate it, so that now the astral and etheric bodies and ego organization are closely united with one another and the physical organism is separate from them."

But what *kind* of thing are all these bodies? We are all too likely now to misread and misunderstand Steiner's real viewpoint. For as Steiner himself emphasized repeatedly, these aspects of the human being are only "bodies" in the sense that they are structured and limited, but not in the sense of having physical or temporal extension. They are thus not *things*, not bodies in our normal sense of the word. Elsewhere Steiner describes the etheric body (also called "life body") as the formative, living *idea* of the plant, animal, or human form. It is not a ghostly cloud of thin matter waving about in the air around a living creature, but the divinely driven concept at its ideal root. Here is Steiner in *Theosophy* on just this confusion of tongues:

> The term "body" is used here to designate what gives a being of any kind its form, shape, or *Gestalt*. It should not be confused with the sense-perceptible form of the material body. As used in this book, the term "body" can also refer to something that takes on form in soul or spirit.

With regard to the related topic of spiritual seeing, Steiner again indicated the ideal or conceptual nature of the process: "We must not confuse the experience itself with its expression in pictorial form." He repeatedly emphasized that concepts such as the various spiritual bodies can be validly approached only

through a schooled consciousness that thinks and feels its way
into the world in a radically new fashion:

> Living thinking must be achieved again. . . . Otherwise we
> shall all the time approach the situation — which we already
> know here and there — in which the knowledge, for
> instance, that the human being has a physical, etheric, and
> astral body will only be known in the form of dead thinking.
> But it must not be understood with dead thinking; for if it is,
> then it is actually a distorted truth and not the truth itself.

We can see this as amplifying this statement in Lecture Ten
of the current volume:

> Humans cannot be known by uncreative thoughts, because
> by their very nature human beings are creative. One must
> re-create if one wants knowledge. With today's passive
> thinking one can only understand the periphery of the
> human being, one has to ignore the inner being.

Using his experience of nonstandard inner structures and
their possible misalignments, Steiner analyzes everything from
sleepwalking to hyperliteracy to the visions of St. Teresa. At certain points he includes the perspective of reincarnation or
"repeated earth lives," and so extends the scope of etiology to
causes of illness that contemporary medicine, theology, and psychology routinely ignore. Here too our normal thinking is inadequate to grasp the meaning of the terms. For it would take an
enlivened sense of *I* (as well as an enlivened sense of *You*) to
know even vaguely what reincarnation means, let alone to investigate the course of a particular personality through several
earthly lives, as Steiner does here with the nineteenth-century
Austrian playwright Ferdinand Raimund.

Discussing the possible disasters of spiritual structure in
this way, Steiner points to the psychological truth that a broken
human being is often a human being who is broken *open*. He

can even call illness a kind of "superspirituality," although it is in need of treatment (Lecture Eight). It was John Dryden who famously wrote that "great wit to madness nearly is allied." Steiner's comments about the opening to spiritual worlds that can accompany severe mental retardation or illness foreshadow some of the most important alternative psychiatry of our own times. He anticipates elements in the work of R. D. Laing, the Windhorse movement of Podvall, and also the new practice of "facilitated communication" whereby some autistic patients have been aided in expressing a full and conscious inner life to which their bizarre outward behavior gives no clue. Another recent contribution that develops this theme appears in Oliver Sacks's story of the twin "idiot savants" who could "see" very large prime numbers although they were unable to calculate the simplest sums.

We can ask in this regard: Why *should* it be the case that our misadjustments, our unrhymedness, our brokenness, sometimes links us to a wider world of understanding or love that reaches beyond life's normal boundaries? The answer lies in the question, for it is indeed a matter of boundaries. When inwardly broken, we may emerge from the network of accustomed concepts that normally paralyzes the world for us. The writer Flannery O'Connor suggested a similar view in her reply to an interviewer who asked her why the best American literature was from the South. "Because we lost the war," she said, meaning the Civil War. The assault on ossified structure led, in some cases, to fruitful openings.

Of course suffering does not necessarily promote creativity, any more than illness necessarily leads to insight, but it *can* do so at times precisely because the "doors of perception," which Blake suggested we cleanse, have instead been selectively battered down, and let in sometimes disastrous quantities of light. In Lecture Two Steiner describes how a "so-called sick man" may come to a priest and reproach him from a position of greater spiritual authority:

"The things you pronounce from the pulpit aren't worth much. They don't add up to anything, they don't reach up to the dwelling place of God, they don't have any worth except external worth. One must really rest in God with one's whole being." That's the kind of thing such people say. In every other area of their life they behave in such a way that one must consider them to be extremely retarded, but in conversation with their priest they come out with such speeches.

One way to think about the poor alignment of inner structures and the great variety of psychic difficulty Steiner describes would be in terms of blockages to wholehearted giving — just as here the man recommends to his priest that one must rest in God with "one's whole being." Throughout his works, Steiner continually emphasizes the fundamental deed of the human being as giving attention to his or her chosen tasks. The more wholly we give, the more we are giving of our *selves* — and our essential self is precisely our attentiveness, for which another name is love. Steiner refers to this issue in innumerable places. Thus, at the end of Lecture Six in the present book, we are told that physicians must "observe these things with their whole being," and that the patients can be helped only when they work "with their whole soul." It is just this that can make healing into what Steiner calls "a divine service." Later he will advocate deeper and deeper immersion in the spiritual beings that permeate and are our cosmos, saying in Lecture Ten that "this is a path of personal development that requires the effort of the whole human being. . . . Not just the head can be engaged . . . but the whole human being is needed."

Such whole giving is, from the standpoint of spiritual structure, equivalent to a process of heightened wakefulness and heightened presence in the world, so that the various supersensible members of the human constitution fuse together. It is a deeply incarnational spirituality. Development consists precisely in *permeating* life processes, and eventually the physical body as well, with a consciousness of eternal presence — not in escaping from this life or this world, but in more wholly entering it. Though in sleep and at death the "ego" (or spiritual self) and the "astral" (or soul) are said by Steiner to disengage from physical and life processes in order to receive nourishment from higher worlds, in initiation the ego and astral can be thought of as joining more intensively with these processes:

> Let us consider first what the situation is when the astral body and ego approach the etheric body. In clairvoyance one can bring this condition about fairly easily, by strengthening one's thinking — strengthening it by very thorough, energetic meditation. Then it is easy to come to this condition; it is the beginning of initiation. One slips down into one's etheric body but is not yet able to take hold of the physical body; one remains in the etheric body. In this condition, it is possible to think very, very well. . . . Thinking becomes wider. One knows clearly: now I am in the etheric world. Thus when one is in one's etheric body, one is truly in the world ether. One has the clear experience: I am in the spiritual world out of which the sense world comes (Lecture Eight).

To enter more wholly into one's body and bodies, to imbue the present world with the full grace of our possible creativity — this is, for Steiner, the ultimate path of both healing and initiation. Along the way, he will throw out further hints in these lectures about the nature of human breathing as a process of bringing in spiritual forces rather than oxygen alone, and about the esoteric nature of sense perception (for a much fuller elaboration of this theme, see Georg Kühlewind's *Belehrung der Sinne*). It is a profoundly Thomistic view in that Thomas Aquinas embraced the physical as divine creation, to be known intimately, rather than as something fallen, to be rejected.

The processes that we are accustomed to think of as physical, as *merely* chemical and physical and biological, can be understood both in the human and in nature as fundamentally meaningful rather than senseless and material. Applying this view radically to the giving of medicines, in Lecture Nine, Steiner can assert, "You can see that one must recognize the spirit in nature, the spirit that is in the mineral and plant kingdoms of the world. It is the spirit, not the substance, that one must know, because in reality one heals the human being through the spirit that is in the mineral and in the plant." In this, Steiner is taking up a theme that the seventeenth-century pastor Angelus Silesius put in a verse (based on John 6:32–35) that has been adapted as a mealtime grace but can also serve as a closing epigraph here:

> The bread does not nourish me.
> What feeds me in the bread
> Is God's eternal Word,
> Is spirit and is life.

MICHAEL LIPSON, PH.D., is a clinical psychologist in independent practice in Great Barrington, Massachusetts. He is the translator of Rudolf Steiner's *Intuitive Thinking as a Spiritual Path* and of Georg Kühlewind's *From Normal to Healthy*, both published by Anthroposophic Press. Dr. Lipson's work combines the insights of Rudolf Steiner with those of Zen Buddhism. He teaches meditation widely, and writes on issues of consciousness, human development, and meditative practice.

Lecture i

For this pastoral medicine course we are bringing members of two distinct circles of spiritual work together for the first time. This is of special importance. We must inquire, therefore, first of all into the reason for the combination, from the intended content of the course itself. In the first place I would like to point out that perhaps this course will be an example of how ancient traditions must be renewed through a particular form of spiritual activity in our time. For what has so far developed under the name "pastoral medicine" has lost its original content. Yet out of the very foundation of this present age there arises a most significant task that as it takes shape may be allowed to bear the name of pastoral medicine.

We have required that this course be mainly for real theologians and real physicians, including those who are training to be real physicians. And both the theologians and the physicians must understand what is now going to be made possible by their working together: a new pastoral medicine. Their working together has indeed often been discussed; it has even been pointed out that the anthroposophical movement should try to bring it about. But things have come to light that must be corrected during this course. A proper working together must certainly not be understood to mean any dilettantish interference by one side into the work of the other side. It certainly does not mean that the theologians are to become physicians, or that the physicians are to become in the slightest way theologians. It is purely a matter of the two professions working together hand-in-hand. The course will stress very strongly the importance of preventing any kind of confusion by, for instance, the theologians trying to get their hands into various medical measures that cannot possibly lie in their sphere of work. On the other hand, physicians must be clearly aware of the position they must always hold — in the sense just described — toward theologians. It is tremendously important that this should be thoroughly understood by both sides. A great deal will depend upon it. Apparently the thought has even been entertained that theologians should actually acquire medical knowledge. Well, of course, it is always good to acquire knowledge. But the important thing here is to realize absolutely clearly that physicians, in addition to the cultivation of their thinking, feeling, and willing, have had specific medical training. People should not play with the idea that they can push their way into the world with bits and pieces of medical knowledge without this specific medical training — even if they are theologians! On the other hand, physicians must develop a special conception of their profession; they must learn through pastoral medicine that something essential is expressed when it is said: The flame of offering belongs to the priest, the Mercury staff to the physician. And only through the working together of the flame of offering and the Mercury staff is a healthful cooperation possible. One must not want to heal with the flame of offering, or to celebrate ritual with the Mercury staff. But one must realize that both are divine service. The more fully this is realized, the better their cooperation will be, with physician remaining physician and priest remaining priest, and the more healing will be their work in the world. Our anthroposophical movement must not be allowed to become an area where everything is thrown together in chaotic fashion: the seriousness that we should be cultivating so strongly within our movement would suffer thereby. One can have knowledge of the general procedure for a foot operation, but one should certainly not think that therefore one can perform the operation. And this holds true for all medical matters. Above all, Anthroposophy must not become propaganda for quackery. Theologians must not be allowed to become quacks.

The Medical Section at the Goetheanum will handle with extreme seriousness whatever is going to give an individual a position out in the world as an anthroposophical physician. But the following must also become an established procedure: that physicians who want to work with the same impulses as the Medical Section at the Goetheanum will have their status and their relation to the Section properly defined by the Section. There will be no progress unless this procedure becomes a complete reality — so complete, in fact, that in the future someone will be acknowledged as a physician if the requirements of the Medical Section at the Goetheanum are filled. From this point of view also, we are justified in not having admitted to this course healers who are not physicians. Those who are here today (with a very few exceptions) can lay full claim in the outside world to membership in the medical profession. Perhaps we have made ourselves clear. I have been speaking more from the administrative angle. But the matter will be the concern of pastoral medicine itself. When the theologians recently raised the question of whether something of a medical nature could be given them, I could not do otherwise than say that I would give a course on pastoral medicine in which theologians could participate. And so the course has been organized by the Medical Section of the Goetheanum, and the theologians are taking part in it. It must be quite clear why we have structured it in this way.

Up to now, pastoral medicine has not been a subject in the medical faculties, but in the theological faculties. And the pastoral medicine that has been taught in the theological faculties has really not contained anything specifically medical. Or perhaps I should ask, have any physicians here who have gone through the academic training had any pastoral medicine in their medical courses? It is not offered in any catalogue of a medical faculty. It hardly appears any more in Protestant theological faculties, but it does have a role in Catholic theological faculties — and for a good reason. Only it contains nothing of a medical nature. In the main it contains, first, the knowledge priests need in order to work as pastors, not only with healthy people who are given into their care, but also with those who are sick. There is a difference in whether one has the care of the soul of a sick person, particularly one who is seriously sick, or of a healthy person. With the sick, perhaps severely sick individuals, the question is how one shapes the soul care, how one relates to it. But I have never yet found a book on pastoral medicine that did not stress repeatedly that the first task of the pastor is to make certain by word and deed that a real doctor is found, and that the pastor should refrain from all medical measures.

A second important subject of pastoral medicine has to do with the hygienic aspects of certain ritual measures. For instance, the healthfulness or unhealthfulness of fasting required for ceremonial reasons is explained for the lay person; also what medical science has to say, for instance, about circumcision and similar matters. For priests themselves — this, of course, has just to do with Catholic faculties — it sets forth clearly what is to be said from a hygienic standpoint about asceticism. This is spoken about very fully.

A further subject has to do with what measures should be taken, for instance, in a parish where there is a doctor, what connection there should be between the medical care and the sacraments. When a religious community bases its activity on the reality of the sacraments, the priest must be prepared to meet the medical treatment that is being given. There is, for instance, the anointing that the priest must perform at the sickbed by the side of the doctor. We have also to consider what significance the earlier pastoral medicine attributed to a person's receiving communion while recovering from a severe illness. Looking at the spiritual aspect, one has to ponder on the working of the sacrament in relation to the processes of healing in a human being.

A further subject examines how the pastor has to relate to the physician in psychopathic cases, cases of mentally handicapped or psychically abnormal individuals. The pastoral work is varied for such cases. This was the principal task confronting pastoral medicine in its earlier days, and it was taken care of through the centuries rather extensively by calling on the authority of the Church Fathers' writings.

That is a field of work that cannot appear in the same light to us who are involved in a renewal of spiritual life. Indeed, from fundamental anthroposophical views we are aware of very important tasks in that field for a new pastoral medicine. And we can discover the extent of such tasks if we consider the subject from two sides.

First, let us consider it from the medical point of view. What are we doing when we apply a therapy? When we give a medicine or apply some healing measure to a sick person, there is always the fact that in the healing process we want to set in motion, whether physical or spiritual or pertaining to the soul, we are going beyond the so-called normal relation of that person to the surrounding world. No matter what therapy we use, in every instance we are going beyond what the person has normally in everyday life, whether it is taking of nourishment, or exposure to light and air, or exposure to soul influences. In every circumstance we are going beyond all of that in our therapy. Even if we simply prescribe a small change of diet, we have gone a small step beyond what the person had permitted in his or her own everyday relation to the surrounding world.

Say we prescribe a medicine. If it's a physical substance, its effect will be that a different process takes place than would take place if the patient were merely eating food. And it is the same with other therapeutic measures. In using any therapeutic measure we are intervening in the life of the patient in a way that is different from the way life usually works upon that person. For what is the normal intervention in human life? How does a person take hold of his or her own life? We can distinguish three kinds of processes that intervene, or can intervene, in human life. First, the process that is active in the person in the same way that physical-chemical forces are active in outer nature. Second, the process that is active in the realm of a person's life forces, in life itself. Third, the process that takes immediate hold of the person in the sphere of consciousness:

1. Physical-chemical
2. Life
3. Consciousness

Here we must grasp an important concept. In ordinary life there are three states of consciousness: waking, dreaming, and sleeping. The moment we apply an active therapeutic measure, we are intervening in the sphere of consciousness to a greater or lesser degree depending on what the measure is. Such intervention never occurs in such a direct way in the so-called normal course of life. A person who is eating, for instance, is surrendering to the usual process of taking nourishment; then, if this has proceeded normally, waking, dreaming, and sleeping follow in normal fashion. At the most, we might vary a diet for the purpose of bringing about better sleep, but there the boundary is already shifted. Therapy has already begun.

It is quite another matter if you intervene with some therapy when, for instance, a patient has a fever. If you were to apply the same therapy to a healthy person you would alter the person's condition of consciousness. Thus a physician has to work fundamentally with the various states of consciousness. A human being's ordinary relation to the outer world has to do with life forces, but in medical work one is intervening in the states of consciousness. You will find this is so in every single therapeutic measure. And it is the specific characteristic of a therapeutic measure that it does enter into what has to do in some way or other with the variability of consciousness. In fact the only effective therapy is one that takes such deep hold of our human constitution that it penetrates to the source from which our various states of consciousness come. But thereby you are intervening as physician, as therapist, directly in the ordering of the spiritual world. Your alteration of someone's condition of consciousness means that you are intervening directly in the ordering of the spiritual world. And when you have a really active cure, through this penetration into the state of consciousness, even though it may be into subconsciousness, you are always drawing the soul of the person into the therapeutic process. You do not remain in the physical sphere. Ordinary consumption of food, ordinary breathing, and other ordinary processes remain in the physical sphere, and the higher members work indirectly through the physical sphere. Higher forces are active through the physical organism. In contrast, when you are working as a physician or therapist you draw the patient's soul directly into his or her physical body. Indeed we can say if physicians understand their profession properly, they realize that they enter directly into the realm of the spiritual. It only seems that therapy is merely a physical or biological process. True therapeutic measures always involve the patient's soul, even though at first this may remain unknown to the ordinary consciousness. You should observe what actually takes place in a patient when, let us say, a fever is suddenly lowered by some therapeutic means. In this event processes are introduced into the innermost depth of the patient's being — just as the illness itself had worked into this depth — beyond the merely physical and biological realm. So we have looked at the picture from the medical point of view. We have seen how doctoring, healing, by its very nature leads from the physical realm into the spiritual.

Now let us examine the priest's profession just as carefully. Priests whose calling is not one of teaching, if they are truly active priests, then they are connected with the ritual, and the ritual includes the sacraments. But the sacraments are not symbols. What are they? They consist of the fact that external events take place, which are not exhausted, in chemical or biological processes. They contain orientations which are embodied in the physical-biological sphere, but which have their origin in the spiritual world. Sense-perceptible actions are performed, and spirit streams into the actions. Spiritual reality is present in the ritual on the level of sense perception. And what takes place there in front of the congregation takes place first of all before their conscious observation. Nothing is permitted to take place except what does take place in that way. Otherwise it would not be ritual, not sacrament, but suggestion. The sacraments — if they are done right — are never allowed to contain any element of suggestion. All the more, therefore, they are able to contain what is spiritual. They take place before the waking consciousness of the participants, but they work into the sphere of the life forces.

In communion a person is not just eating the material substance; in that case it would not be a sacrament. Nor is it a matter of symbols. Rather it has to do with reaching into a person's life, because a sacrament is enacted, is celebrated, through an orientation toward the spiritual world. Therefore one can say therapy leads from life to consciousness; the ritual with its sacraments leads from consciousness to life.

Therapy: life to consciousness
Ritual (sacraments): consciousness to life

There you have the two activities in polarity: therapeutic activity and the celebration of the sacraments. In therapeutic measures, the course leads from life to consciousness, and consciousness becomes a helper, at least (in ordinary consciousness) an unconscious helper, in the healing process. In the celebration of the sacraments life is made a helper for what is enacted before the consciousness. Both of these activities have to be grasped spiritually in deep inwardness — not merely diagrammatically as it is now being presented to you. They require the involvement of the total human being if that individual wants to make one or the other a vocation. In our present civilization therapy has left behind the spiritual element, and theology has left behind the concrete world. In our present civilization therapy has taken a false path into materialism and theology a false path into abstraction. For these reasons their true relationship has become completely veiled. This true relationship must be reestablished. It must become active again.

Again it must become clear that for diagnosis physicians need a trained observation that enables them to see a biological or physical process in the human organism as a spiritual process.

For all processes in the human organism are spiritual. For diagnosing, and still more for treatment, physicians need an observation that is trained to see the lighting up of the spirit within the physical. Priests need an observation that is trained to see the lighting up of the physical reflection of a spiritual event. There is a polarity again. But there must always be polarities working together in this world, and these are no exception.

To see how they are to work together will be a task within the sphere of Anthroposophy and based on Anthroposophy, a task also to be fulfilled within anthroposophical spheres of activity. So one can think that out of this gathering for a pastoral medicine course there may actually be created future anthroposophical physicians — physicians who will hold the right relation to priests because of their own relation to the spiritual world. The priests themselves will have come out of the Movement for Religious Renewal. Something quite special will develop out of this course for the physician and the priest so that they will work together in a true way.

For what in this case can it mean that they work together? Surely not that the priest does dilettantish doctoring and that the doctor is a dilettante priest! If their working together were to consist of priests knowing a few medical facts and physicians vesting themselves as priests, then I'd like to know why they should work together. Why should an experienced physician be interested in half priest–half doctor dilettantism? It makes no sense. And why should a priest want to interfere in medical matters except when the physician asks for a pastor? On the other hand, if the physician is a good physician standing squarely within the medical profession, and if the priest is a real priest, they can work together. It means that one offers help to the other out of professional abilities, not that one pushes into the other's professional domain.

Such an association will bring about a profoundly important result for our culture. The physician will truly understand the priest, and the priest the physician. The priest will know as much about being a doctor as is needed to know and the physician as much about the vocation of the priest as is needed to know. And then in time we will see to what extent physician and priest can work with the teacher to accomplish something beneficial to humanity.

In that area, too, people will have to work together — and in the most manifold ways, because education is also something that must be looked at from a fresh point of view. The priest cannot be a physician, nor the physician a priest, but they can both in a certain sense be teachers. But all the details of these new associations will have to be thought out quite concretely. Therefore I would like to ask you from the very beginning to count this earnest request as part of all that this pastoral medicine course is going to present: that everything be worked out on a professional and expert basis. Priests will truly help actual physicians if they reject all thought of medical dilettantism. That will be one of their responsibilities. And physicians will be able to do very much at the sickbed to bring the mission of the priests to proper fulfillment — precisely at the sickbed, where often a priest has to intervene in life in a really essential way.

LECTURE 2

IF WE ARE GOING TO CONSIDER the mutual concerns of priest and physician, we should look first at certain phenomena in human life that easily slide over into the pathological field. These phenomena require a physician's understanding, since they reach into profound depths, even into the esoteric realm of religious life. We have to realize that all branches of human knowledge must be liberated from a certain coarse attitude that has come into them in this materialistic epoch. We need only recall how certain phenomena that had been grouped together for some time under the heading "genius and insanity" have recently been given a crass interpretation by Lombroso[1] and his school and also by others. I am not pointing to the research itself — that has its uses — but rather to their way of looking at things, to what they brought out as "criminal anthropology," from studying the skulls of criminals. The opinions they voiced were not only coarse but extraordinarily commonplace. Obviously the philistines all got together and decided what the normal type of human being is. And it was as near as could possibly be to a philistine! And whatever deviated from this type was pathological, genius on one side, insanity on the other; each in its own way was pathological. Since it is quite obvious to anyone with insight that every pathological characteristic also expresses itself bodily, it is also obvious that symptoms can be found in bodily characteristics pointing in one or the other direction. It is a matter of regarding the symptoms in the proper way. Even an earlobe can under certain conditions clearly reveal some psychological peculiarity, because such psychological peculiarities are connected with the karma that works over from earlier incarnations.

The forces that build the physical organism in the first seven years of human life are the same forces by which we think later. So it is important to consider certain phenomena, not in the customary manner but in a really appropriate way. We will not be regarding them as pathological (although they will lead us into aspects of pathology) but rather will be using them to obtain a view of human life itself.

Let us for a moment review the picture of a human being that Anthroposophy gives us. The human being stands before us in a physical body, which has a long evolution behind it, three preparatory stages before it became an earthly body — as is described in my book *An Outline of Esoteric Science*.[2] This earthly body needs to be understood much more than it is by today's anatomy and physiology. For the human physical body as it is today is a true image of the etheric body, which is in its third stage of development, and of the astral body, which is in its second stage, and even to a certain degree of the ego organization that humans first received on earth, which therefore is in its first stage of development. All of this is stamped like the stamp of a seal upon the physical body — which makes the physical body extraordinarily complicated. Only its purely mineral and physical nature can be understood with the methods of knowledge that are brought to it today. What the etheric body impresses upon it is not to be reached at all by those methods. It has to be observed with the eye of a sculptor so that one obtains pictorial images of cosmic forces, images that can then be recognized again in the form of the entire human being and in the forms of the single organs.

The physical human being is also an image of the breathing and blood circulation. But the entire dynamic activity that works and weaves through the blood circulation and breathing system can only be understood if one thinks of it in musical forms. For instance, there is a musical character to the formative forces that were poured into the skeletal system and then became active in a finer capacity in the breathing and circulation. We can perceive in eurythmy how the octave goes out from the shoulder blade and proceeds along the bones of the arm. This bone formation of the arm cannot be understood from a mechanical view of dynamics, but only from musical insight. We

find the interval of the prime extending from the shoulder blade
to the bone of the upper arm, the humerus, the interval of the
second in the humerus, the third from the elbow to the wrist.
We find two bones there because there are two thirds in music,
a larger and a smaller. And so on. In short, if we want to find the
impression of the astral body upon the physical body, upon the
breathing and blood circulation, we are obliged to bring a musical understanding to it.

Still more difficult to understand is the ego organization.
For this one needs to grasp the meaning of the first verse of
the Gospel of St. John: "In the beginning was the Word."
"The Word" is meant there to be understood in a concrete
sense, not abstractly, as commentators of the Gospels usually
present it. If this is applied concretely to the real human
being, it provides an explanation of how the ego organization
penetrates the human physical body. You can see that we
ought to add much more to our studies if they are to lead to a
true understanding of the human being. However, I am convinced that a tremendous amount of material could be elimi-
nated not only from medical courses but from theological
courses too. If one would only assemble the really essential
material, the number of years medical students, for instance,
must spend in their course would not be lengthened but
shortened. Naturally it is thought in materialistic fashion
today that if there's something new to be included, you must
tack another half-year onto the course!

Out of the knowledge that Anthroposophy gives us, we can
say that the human being stands before us in physical, etheric
and astral bodies, and an ego organization. In waking life these
four members of the human organization are in close
connection. In sleep the physical body and etheric body are
together on one side, and the ego organization and astral body
on the other side. With knowledge of this fact we are then able
to say that the greatest variety of irregularities can appear in the
connection of ego organization and astral body with etheric
body and physical body. For instance, we can have: physical

body, etheric body, astral body, ego organization. Then, in the waking state, the so-called normal relation prevails among these four members of the human organization.

But it can also happen that the physical body and etheric body are in some kind of normal connection and that the astral body sits within them comparatively normally, but that the ego organization is somehow not properly sitting within the astral body. Then we have an irregularity that in the first place confronts us in the waking condition. Such people are unable to come with their ego organization properly into their astral body; therefore their feeling life is very much disturbed. They can even form quite lively thoughts. For thoughts depend, in the main, upon a normal connection of the astral body with the other bodies. But whether the sense impressions will be grasped appropriately by the thoughts depends upon whether the ego organization is united with the other parts in a normal fashion. If not, the sense impressions become dim. And in the same measure that the sense impressions fade, the thoughts become livelier. Sense impressions can appear almost ghostly, not clear as we normally have them. The soul-life of such people is flowing away; their sense impressions have something misty about them, they seem to be continually vanishing. At the same time their thoughts have a lively quality and tend to become more intense, more colored, almost as if they were sense impressions themselves.

When such people sleep, their ego organization is not properly within the astral body, so that now they have extraordinarily strong experiences, in fine detail, of the external world around them. They have experiences, with their ego and astral body both outside their physical and etheric bodies, of that part of the world in which they live — for instance, the finer details of the plants or an orchard around their house. Not what they see during the day, but the delicate flavor of the apples, and so forth. That is really what they experience. And in addition, pale thoughts that are after-effects in the astral body from their waking life.

You see, it is difficult if you have such a person before you. And you may encounter such people in all variations in the most manifold circumstances of life. You may meet them in your vocation as physician or as priest — or the whole congregation may encounter them. You can find them in endless variety, for instance, in a town. Today the physician who finds such a person in an early stage of life makes the diagnosis: psychopathological impairment.

To modern physicians that person is a psychopathological impairment case who is at the borderline between health and illness; whose nervous system, for instance, can be considered to be on a pathological level. Priests, if they are well-schooled (let us say a Benedictine or Jesuit or Barnabite or the like; ordinary parish priests are sometimes not so well-schooled), will know from their esoteric background that the things such a person tells them can, if properly interpreted, give genuine revelations from the spiritual world, just as one can have from a really insane person. But the insane person is not able to interpret them; only someone who comprehends the whole situation can do so. Thus you can encounter such a person if you are a physician, and we will see how to regard this person medically from an anthroposophical point of view. Thus you can also encounter such a person if you are a priest — and even the entire congregation can have such an encounter.

But now perhaps the person develops further; then something quite special appears. The physical and etheric bodies still have their normal connection. But now there begins to be a stronger pull of the ego organization, drawing the astral body to itself, so that the ego organization and astral body are now more closely bound together. And neither of them enters properly into the physical and etheric bodies. Then the following can take place: the person becomes unable to control the physical and etheric bodies properly from the astral body and ego. The person is unable to push the astral body and ego organization properly into the external senses, and therefore, every now and then, becomes "senseless." Sense impressions in general fade away and the person falls into a kind of dizzy dream state. But then in the most varied way moral impulses can appear with special strength. The person can be confused and also extremely argumentative if the rest of the organism is as just described.

Now physicians find in such a case that physical and biochemical changes have taken place in the sense organs and the nerve substance. They will find, although they may take slight notice of them, great abnormalities in the ductless glands and their hormone secretion, in the adrenal glands, and the glands that are hidden in the neck as small glands within the thyroid gland. In such a case there are changes particularly in the pituitary gland and the pineal gland. These are more generally recognized than are the changes in the nervous system and in the general area of the senses.

And now the priest comes in contact with such a person. The person confesses to experiencing an especially strong feeling of sin, stronger than people normally have. The priest can learn very much from such individuals, and Catholic priests do. They learn what an extreme consciousness of sin can be like, something that is so weakly developed in most human beings. Also in such a person the love of one's neighbor can become tremendously intense, so much so that the person can get into great trouble because of it, which will then be confessed to the priest.

The situation can develop still further. The physical body can remain comparatively isolated because the etheric body — from time to time or even permanently — does not entirely penetrate it, so that now the astral and etheric bodies and the ego organization are closely united with one another and the physical organism is separate from them. To use the current materialistic terms (which we are going to outgrow as the present course of study progresses), such people are in most cases said to be severely mentally retarded individuals. They are unable from their soul-spiritual individuality to control their physical limbs in any direction, not even in the direction of their own will. Such people pull their physical organism along, as it were, after themselves. A person who is in this condition in early childhood, from birth, is also diagnosed as mentally retarded. In the present stage of earth evolution, when all three members — ego organization, astral organization, and etheric body — are separated from the physical, and the lone physical body is dragged along after them, the person cannot perceive, cannot be active, cannot be illumined by the ego organization, astral body, and etheric body. So experiences are dim and the person goes about in a physical body as if it were anesthetized. This is extreme mental retardation, and one has to think how at this stage one can bring the other bodies down into the physical organism. Here it can be a matter of educational measures, but also to a great extent of external therapeutic measures.

But now the priest can be quite amazed at what such a person will confess. Priests may consider themselves very clever, but even thoroughly educated priests — there really are such men in Catholicism; one must not underestimate it — they pay attention if a so-called sick person comes to them and says, "The things you pronounce from the pulpit aren't worth much. They don't add up to anything, they don't reach up to the dwelling place of God, they don't have any worth except external worth. One must really rest in God with one's whole being." That's the kind of thing such people say. In every other area of their life they behave in such a way that one must consider them to be extremely retarded, but in conversation with their priest they come out with such speeches. They claim to know inner religious life more intimately than someone who speaks of it professionally; they feel contempt for the professional. They call their experience "rest in God." And you can see that the priest must find ways and means to relate to what such a person — one can say patient, or one can use other terms — to what such a human being is experiencing within.

One has to have a sensitive understanding for the fact that pathological conditions can be found in all spheres of life, for the fact that some people may be quite unable at the present time to find their way in the physical-sense world, quite unable to be the sort of human being that external life now requires all of us to be. We are all necessarily to a certain degree philistines as regards external life. But such people as I am describing are not in condition to travel along our philistine paths; they have to travel other ways. Priests must be able to feel what they can give such a person, how to connect what they can give out of themselves with what that other human being is experiencing. Very often such a person is simply called "one of the queer ones." This demands an understanding of the subtle transition from illness to spirituality.

Our study can go further. Think what happens when a person goes through this entire sequence in the course of life. At some period the person is in a condition where only the ego organization has loosened itself from the other members of the organism. In a later period the person advances to a condition where neither ego nor astral enter the physical or etheric bodies. Still later, the person enters a condition where the physical body separates from the other bodies. The person only goes through this sequence if the first condition, perhaps in childhood, which is still normal, already shows a tendency to lose the balance of the four members of the organism. If the physician comes upon such a person destined to go through all these four stages — the first very slightly abnormal, the others as I have pictured them — the physician will find there is tremendous instability and something must be done about it. Usually nothing can be done. Sometimes the physician prescribes intensive treatment; it accomplishes nothing. Perhaps later the physician is again in contact with this person and finds that the first unstable condition has advanced to the next, as I described it with the sense impressions becoming vague and the thoughts highly colored. Eventually the physician finds the excessively strong consciousness of sin; naturally a physician does not want to take any notice of that, for now the symptoms are beginning to play over into the soul realm. Usually it is at this time that the person finally gets in touch with a priest, particularly when the fourth stage becomes apparent.

Individuals who go through these stages — it is connected with their karma, their repeated earth lives — have purely out of their deep intuition developed a wonderful terminology for all this. Especially if they have gone through the stages in sequence, with the first stage almost normal, they are able to speak in a wonderful way about what they experience. They say, for instance, when they are still quite young, if the labile condition starts between seventeen and nineteen years: human beings must know themselves. And they demand complete knowledge of themselves. Now with their ego organization separated, they come of their own initiative to an active meditative life. Very often they call this "active prayer," "active meditation," and they are grateful when some well-schooled priest gives them instruction about prayer. Then they are entirely absorbed in prayer, and they are experiencing in it what they now begin to describe by a wonderful terminology. They look back at their first stage and call what they perceive "the first dwelling place of God," because their ego has not entirely penetrated the other members of their organism, so to a certain extent they are seeing themselves from within, not merely from without. This perception from within increases; it becomes, as it were, a larger space: "the first dwelling place of God."

What next appears, what I have described from another point of view, is richer; it is more inwardly detailed. They see much more from within: "the second dwelling place of God." When the third stage is reached, the inner vision is extraordinarily beautiful, and such a person says, "I see the third dwelling place of God; it is tremendously magnificent, with spiritual beings moving within it." This is inner vision, a powerful, glorious vision of a world woven by spirit: "the third dwelling place of God," or "the House of God." There are variations in the words used. When they reach the fourth stage, they no longer want advice about active meditation, for usually they have reached the view that everything will be given them through grace and they must wait. They talk about passive prayer, passive meditation, that they must not pray out of their own initiative, for it will come to them if God wants to give it to them. Here the priest must have a fine instinct for recognizing when this stage passes over into the next. For now these people speak of "rest-prayer," during which they do nothing at all; they let God hold sway in them. That is how they experience "the fourth dwelling place of God."

Sometimes from the descriptions they give at this stage, from what — if we speak medically — such "patients" say, priests can really learn a tremendous amount of esoteric theology. If they are good interpreters, the theological detail becomes clear to them — if they listen very carefully to what such "patients" tell them, to what they know. Much of what is taught in theology, particularly Catholic pastoral theology, is founded on what various enlightened, trained confessors have heard from certain penitents who have undergone this sequence of development.

At this point ordinary conceptions of health and illness cease to have any meaning. If such a man is hidden away in an office, or if such a woman becomes an housewife who must spend her days in the kitchen or something similar in bourgeois everyday life, these people become really insane, and behave outwardly in such a way that they can only be regarded as insane. If a priest notices at the right moment how things are developing and arranges for them to live in appropriate surroundings, they can develop the four stages in proper order. Through such patients, the enlightened confessor is able to look into the spiritual world in a modern way but similarly to the Greek priests, who learned about the spiritual world from the Pythians, who imparted all kinds of revelations concerning the spiritual world through earthly smoke and vapor.[3] What sense would there be today in writing a thesis on the pathological aspect of the Greek Pythians? It could certainly be done and it would even be correct, but it would have no meaning in a higher sense. For as a matter of fact, very much of what flowed in a magnificent way from Greek theology into the entire cultural life of Greece originated in the revelations of the Pythians. As a rule, the Pythians were individuals who had come either to this third stage or even to the fourth stage.

But we can think of a personality in a later epoch who went through these stages under the wise direction of her confessors, so that she could devote herself undisturbed to her inner visions. Something very wonderful developed for her, which indeed also remained to a certain degree pathological. Her life was not just a concern of the physician or of the priest but a concern of the entire Church. The Church pronounced her a saint after her death. This was St. Teresa.[4] This was approximately her path.

You see, one must examine such things as this if one wants to discover what will give medicine and theology a real insight into human nature. One must be prepared to go far beyond the usual category of ideas, for they lose their value. Otherwise one can no longer differentiate between a saint and a fool, between a madman and a genius, and can no longer distinguish any of the others except a normal dyed-in-the-wool average citizen.

This is a view of the human being that must first be met with understanding; then it can really lead to fundamental esoteric knowledge. But it can also be tremendously enlightening in regard to psychological abnormalities as well as to physical abnormalities and physical illnesses. Certain conditions are necessary for these stages to appear. There has to be a certain consistency of the person's ego so that it does not completely penetrate the organism. Also there must be a certain consistency of the astral body: if it is not fine, as it was in St. Teresa, if it is coarse, the result will be different. With St. Teresa, because of the delicacy of her ego organization and astral body, certain physical organs in the lower body had been formed with the same fragile quality.

But it can happen that the ego organization and astral body are quite coarse and yet they have the same characteristic as above. Such an individual can be comparatively normal and show only the physical correlation: then it is only a physical illness. One could say, on the one hand there can be a St. Teresa constitution with its visions and poetic beauty, and on the other hand its physical counterimage in diseased abdominal organs, which in the course of this second person's life is not reflected in the ego and astral organization.

All these things must be spoken about and examined. For those who hold responsibility as physicians or priests are confronted by these things, and they must be equal to the challenge. Theological activity only begins to be effective if theologians are prepared to cope with such phenomena. And physicians only begin to be healers if they also are prepared to deal with such symptoms.

LECTURE 3

WE WILL OBTAIN A DEEPER VIEW of the total human being if we go a little further into the matters we have been considering. In particular, we should see from such symptoms how important the transition is from health to illness. I therefore would like to speak further about something that lies between certain pathological trends that are developing in human evolution and a kind of natural initiation that constitutes another stream in human evolution. This phenomenon lies midway between the pathological tendencies of human nature and the stream of initiation; it relates as much to one as to the other.

Typical of such a path of development are such personalities as St. Teresa. One can observe much more than I described if one makes a study of some of these individuals. With them there is a kind of appearance of the spiritual world at the threshold of perception. Naturally this is difficult to describe, because the words one has to use to characterize these abnormal conditions do not have such meanings in our everyday speech. What appears at the threshold of perception is the first stage for such people and is called by them "entrance into the first dwelling place of God." In the first stage this is perceived only as "a presence." These people experience the presence of some spiritual being, but they have no precise vision of the being. If the experience comes to a definite conclusion, they have a clear feeling that the being was there with them. That is the first experience: an indefinite experience of a presence, of being together with some spiritual being. As long as they are in this stage of development, these people are even annoyed when someone else tells them of a vision, because these people think their own experience is much more inward, much more intimate, more genuine. This has been such a moving experience for them that they have the feeling: human beings are not allowed to see the supersensible world, but I have been given this vague experience of its reality.

Then these people reach a second stage. They tell of actual, shaped perceptions of the spiritual beings that were present. First they tell of the feeling of being touched, of having spiritual hands laid upon them, even of their forehead being touched or something similar, without yet having any visual experience. Then the condition is raised to vision that is like optical perception. It can be so enhanced that they see Jesus, for instance, standing before them as a real person. That is the usual second stage. It is a peculiar fact that those advancing from the first to the second stage have only the vaguest feeling that earlier they had become angry when others told them of their own experiences in this second stage. Memory does not clearly connect the two stages. These people live very intensely in the respective single stages.

The third stage they experience is remarkable. Their description of it is highly colored in every detail. They tell how when it comes upon them they are seized by tremendous pain. And indeed it is obviously intense, for at these moments they can be heard groaning; other reactions can be observed such as occur with pain originating in the physical and etheric bodies. But the strange thing is that they *want* this pain. They want it because they regard it as natural that they should have it; they feel that they will only reach the subsequent experience properly if first they suffer this pain.

Then they reach the stage where they transform the pain within themselves. This is extraordinarily interesting, for actually the pain remains exactly the same, but now it is enhanced into a feeling of joy, of bliss. The pain comes, its objective condition is still there, but now the spiritual awareness goes further. If one were suddenly to pull such people out of their spiritual state, they would feel the pain as sick people feel pain — and indeed do so when they return from this highest stage of the experience. At this highest stage they no longer have the feeling that spiritual beings come to them, but that they themselves have risen into the spiritual world. At this stage the pain is transformed — one might say subjectively, but the expression is not quite exact — into a feeling of bliss. Then begins a symbolic objectifying of the pain. When they come out of this experience and have a memory of it (and in most cases there is a very clear memory of it afterward), then they describe how a seraph or a cherub stood beside them, and the seraph or cherub had a sword that he plunged into the their intestines, which caused excruciating pain. When the spiritual being pulled out the sword he pulled the intestines out too, and then there came immediately an experience of profound bliss in the presence of God.

As a rule these three stages follow in succession. We can understand them clearly through our anthroposophical knowledge. After the preparatory condition I have described, the first stage consists of the ego organization drawing the astral body to itself, so that they are united without penetrating the physical and etheric bodies as deeply as they normally would. Something, therefore, is happening for such persons that can never happen in ordinary consciousness: in half-waking or quarter-waking or three-quarters waking condition they have conscious experience in their ego organization and astral body, while at the same time experience in their etheric and physical bodies continues with a certain independence. Thus parallel experiences are there: a spiritual experience in the ego organization and astral body, and at the same time a separate experience of the etheric and physical bodies. This is never the case in normal consciousness: there, all four members of the human being are bound closely together. In normal consciousness there is no such thing as experiences of consciousness running parallel. In this experience I am describing, such people feel themselves, know themselves in the most eminent sense to be entirely united with what they are experiencing. They know this first of all, the inherent being-one-with the happening. When the astral body is drawn to the ego organization and experiences spiritual beings, these people experience them as simply a presence, as something that is there. They experience this as one experiences one's own body. One does not differentiate in the latter experience. One does not feel one's body as something outside: one feels it as part of oneself. That is the first stage: the experience of "a presence."

Now let us go to the second stage. First, these people have all kinds of feelings of being touched. Naturally these can be confused very easily by ordinary pathology with familiar psychiatric symptoms, but they are not the same. Then they advance to actual visions. This is the stage where the ego organization and astral organization draw the etheric body out to be united with them. So again there is a parallel experience: the ego organization, astral organization, and etheric body are all raised somewhat out of the physical body; at the same time the physical body carries on its processes separately. Something special comes about through this situation. In ordinary life, when we see, we are stimulated by light from without and we receive the stimulus into ourselves. It goes as far as the etheric body, and the etheric body creates the conscious experience. That is how it is, for example, with the eyes. When you see, the external stimulation occurs first in the ego; then it penetrates the astral body and penetrates the etheric body. It is then the etheric body that communicates the whole conscious experience to you by pushing in every direction, in a certain sense, against the physical organization. The conscious experience lies in this pushing. That is the exact process. If presented in a diagram, it would look like the drawing below.

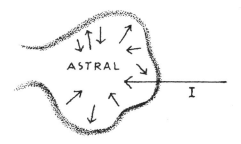

ASTRAL

I

A stimulus is exerted. First it affects the ego, then it goes to the astral body, then to the etheric body; in the etheric body it pushes into the physical body in every direction, to all sides. The physical body pushes back, and the pushing back, the repulsion by the physical body, is your actual eye experience. It is a constant play between the etheric body and the choroid and retina. What the etheric body does in the choroid and in the retina is what appears to ordinary consciousness as optical experience. This happens similarly with every other sense perception. To anyone who understands these things, the entire explanation in today's psychology textbooks, or even in epistemology, is terribly childish.

But now, with such people as I am describing, the etheric body is seized directly in this experience. The experience sits in the ego, astral body, etheric body, and does not push out to the senses, but pushes from within to what is the nerve-sense system — pushes first, actually, into the glandular system, then into the nervous system, and finally from there streams into the senses. So the senses are taken hold of in a way that is just the opposite of the way it happens in ordinary life. Instead of the experience of consciousness being stimulated through the senses, it is colored, intensified, made vivid by the fact that it streams from within to the senses. That is how the feeling of being touched comes about in a sensation of the nerves: by the streaming from within outward. This is then raised to vision. Now you know the whole inner process.

If there is a further development, it proceeds in the following way: the ego organization, astral body, and etheric body take hold of the physical body from quite another direction than would normally be the case. The physical body is accustomed to being taken hold of from without, but now it is taken hold of from within. Now it is taken hold of in the midst of life — the very process that otherwise only happens when the human soul-spiritual entity comes down out of the soul-spiritual world into the physical body, three weeks after conception. This event cannot otherwise happen in ordinary life, because normally the etheric body is connected with the physical body. But in this case the etheric body has been raised out by the ego organization and taken hold of by the astral body. It is like birth, when the human being takes possession of a physical body, but now the procedure is more complicated, possessing this physical body from quite another direction. And that causes pain. For as a matter of fact, all pain — in cases of illness, too — consists of the fact that the body is grasped hold of from some other direction than the usual one. That is what happens at the moment when the third stage is reached.

Now you need not be surprised that this third stage is objectified. It penetrates the physical body and the physical body repels it. A physical body cannot be so seized except in regular initiation; in any other situation the physical body exerts opposition, and this causes pain. It pushes away in pain what it is experiencing. That is the first part of the experience of the third stage. The physical body exerts resistance and the resistance is experienced as pain. And what enters through the pain? The real spiritual world. It comes through the pain. The spiritual world comes from the other direction. Ordinary sense perception and ordinary thinking grasp hold of the physical world. The spiritual world is grasped in the opposite way. The way to it is through pain. The moment the physical body exerts resistance, intense pain is there. But the moment the pain is taken hold of by the spiritual world, the moment the spiritual world enters, the pain is transformed into ecstasy. It is really so. First there is pain in the organism; then the spiritual world penetrates the pain, streams through the pain: a cherub or seraph appears (this is what the imagination presents), the cherub plunges his sword in, draws it out, and draws the intestines out with it. This means that the person becomes independent of the physical body, of the ordinary connection to it. The person has no experience in the lower organs and is led beyond it to an experience of the spiritual world. The physical pain is transformed to bliss. Such people speak of the presence of God, or if they make distinctions, of the presence of the spiritual world.

This last stage is experienced by individuals who are strong enough in their etheric body to endure the entire happening. They have the foundation for it in their karma. For instance, think of St. Teresa. She had an earlier incarnation in which her soul became especially strong. She incarnates as St. Teresa. But before she incarnates in the physical body, she takes possession of her etheric body very forcefully, and this etheric body becomes inwardly stronger than is the case with the usual human being. She has brought it with her into this life, this etheric body that is inwardly strong. Then this strong etheric body leaves the physical body and unites itself firmly with the astral body and ego, which are also especially strong from an earlier incarnation. And that is why illnesses then appear, at least a certain variety of illness: because the etheric body is not staying in the physical organs and providing them with its nourishing, vitalizing forces. With the individuals I am describing, the moment they enter the third stage they become really ill. At the same time their strong etheric body enables them to overcome the illness as it is developing. The illness begins to develop and immediately an automatic therapy arises within them from the strong etheric body. The entire process is a latent illness and healing. This is one of the most interesting phenomena in the realm of human evolution.

Precisely in the case of St. Teresa you see in the final stage of her development a continual *status nascendi* of illness and the continual cure. This alternation, this wonderful swing of a pendulum between the beginning of illness and the caring of it, is not a natural happening in the physical world, for it is not brought about in the physical world: it takes place in the spiritual world. We know that the etheric body is formed before the earthly incarnation. And it is into that pre-earthly moment that such a person as St. Teresa returns. When the pathological condition starts, when it is *in statu nascendi*, she "swings" into the world where she was before birth, into the spiritual world. The pendulum swings between the physical body and the spiritual world. Spiritual world — physical world — spiritual world —

physical world, but experiencing the physical world as an exact opposite — such as normally human beings only experience when they are just incarnating into it. This inner process of healing, this therapy coming from the cosmos, is so intense that its effect can spread to sick people who are in the neighborhood of such people, if their illness lies somewhat in the same direction. In fact, the most wonderful cures can take place around such a person.

Indeed the influence can extend much further. In the former, better days of the church, these things were used in a careful, esoteric way. Later this degenerated to a superstitious worship of relics and belief in magic. But it is a fact that in better times of religious evolution, vivid biographies of such individuals, including their own imaginative descriptions, were given to the faithful, so that they could live through the experiences of such people in their own imagination. And it could then happen that when thoughtful pastors had the opportunity, they would simply put such a biography into the hands of someone in ordinary life whose illness was going in a certain direction. Perhaps also they strengthened the effect by their own words, and this was able to start curative processes. Directing the sick individual's mind to the life of such a saint could have a therapeutic effect.

You can see that studies that go so deeply into the human being will always lead from health to illness, but also to states of supersensible experience. If therefore you advise someone in some connection or other to do exercises to gain entrance into the supersensible world, the exercises must be so oriented that they strengthen the ego organization, astral body, and etheric body. Such a path as I described, given to individuals simply through their karma, will in fact take its course properly. What takes place in initiation itself can be learned by studying these processes, which border so closely on the pathological. Therefore it is not unimportant for physicians to take the time to study the lives of such people. Physicians will find in them what can only be called a paradox: the healthy counterpart of a complex of pathological symptoms that they are accustomed to meet here and there in everyday life. And for physicians, that is the most beneficial thing possible: to see the healthy counterpart of a pathological condition. That, more than anything else, will help physicians to make thoughtful, conscientious decisions about their therapy. Moreover if physicians have some knowledge of the substance that can be used as a remedy because of its affinity to certain etheric forces — forces that automatically become active in the self-healing of these abnormal individuals — they will know how St. Teresa's etheric body developed its forces when her illnesses appeared *in statu nascendi*. And if physicians learn to know the healing power to be found in the piercing activity of antimony, then they will have learned the right therapy from Nature herself.

I would like to point out that in examining such experiences as these, one encounters a remarkable paradox: one sees illness from another side. One sees illness being treated not by human beings but by spiritual beings. One kind of treatment is the kind human beings evolve: that is, treatment from the aspect of the earth. It consists of restoring the previous condition through some therapy that breaks up the illness. The spiritual beings that have to do with humanity treat illness differently. They weave an illness into the fabric of karma. That is their task — a task that doesn't pile things together as they are piled together here on earth by pathology. Here a seventeen-year-old who is ill is not always cured by forty-five. But with the way karma is formed, an illness in some incarnation, whether it is cured or not, may be woven into the human being's karma three thousand years later. Time is measured quite differently in the spiritual world. But one learns very much from those developments in which, from a spiritual point of view, something can happen in the spiritual world and then can also stream down into the physical world.

Take, for example, such a form of karma as I have been describing. Perhaps it is completely in the ordinary course of evolution in three thousand years. Let me show by this line

3000 YEARS

(see drawing above) that something that happens to a person today is so shaped by spiritual beings that the other part belonging to it, the balance, the compensation, appears in three thousand years' time. That is the normal course. You see, in ordinary life people don't have a true knowledge of time. How do they think of it ordinarily? As a line running from past infinity through the present into the future. That is approximately how time is imagined — and indeed, the line has to be thick — perhaps not even a line, but a thick rope, because it contains everything that is perceived at any given moment in the whole world. That's the way people think of it if they think of it at all — and most people don't think of it at all. From a spiritual point of view time is not like that. And one finds little understanding for spiritual development — which, after all, is present in all physical evolution — when time is thought of in that conventional way. In reality, time is different. The line I drew on the board can be tangled up into a ball (see drawing). The entire line of time is in that ball. Three thousand years are in that ball. Time can be all tangled up; and if it is tangled up for some development or other in evolution, then the tangle can be found in the life of some individual. In the case of St. Teresa, a tangled ball of time was present in her earthly life. We come upon a true mystery — that things that in someone's karma would seem to be widely separate for some reason become entangled.

You see from such an example how a study of the inner spiritual, karmic development must link up with the external pathological and therapeutic inquiry. You can see how the pas-

toral care of some person by priests, who are basing their view of
the person on the karmic connections, the spiritual aspects, can
relate to what is seen from a medical view alone. For a comprehension of these things requires not only theoretical knowledge
but really living into the things. Physicians must live into them
on the pathological, physiological side that opens up for them.
Priests must live into them in the theological and karmic views
that open up for them. And the harmony will come from their
working together out of these two different fields, not from
interfering in each other's field in a dilettantish fashion. This
must be stressed again and again.

You must still see something else that is connected with
these things, particularly in our epoch. You know how distaste-
ful it is to some people to accept the idea of free will even
though it is perfectly obvious to an unbiased person. The
philosophers deny its reality because their intellect can't make a
connection with it. I said just now in regard to sense perceptions that the explanations in physiology and psychology textbooks are absolutely childish to someone who understands
these things. But the chatter over free will is far worse. For you
must remember: a decision of free will is at every moment an
act of the whole human being — the whole human being — no
matter how they appear in this impulse: healthy or ill or half ill
or abnormally healthy. The whole human being is involved in
an impulse of free will — and, all that can be known of the
whole human being, all the complications. One only learns to
know human nature when one learns to know it with all its
complications. And please notice, something that in an abnormal person shows too strong a color in one or another direction
is neutralized, harmonized in the ordinary human being.
There's a trivial expression, but it's true: A cherub can make
friends with you, but the devil can too. And those processes
where the devil can squeeze in — we're going to study them
too! This is all to be found in the ordinary human being, but
opposing forces are neutralized, because they develop equally
strongly in every direction. If there's an angel in every human,

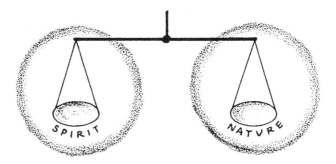

there's also a devil. But when the angel and the devil are equally strong, they neutralize each other.

Now take a look at these scales (see drawing). There is one spot, one point right here. You can lay weights there or there and then you have put the scales into movement. But this spot always remains still. It has a name: the hypomochlion. It is not affected by what you lay on the scale at the left, or what you lay on the scale at the right. Of course, the scales must be built so that this spot will not need to be disturbed. Now in the human being a similar spiritual hypomochlion is created by the opposing forces. Therefore you can study human nature and you will never be able to call human beings free, for by their very nature they are causally conditioned in all respects.

If you study the nature of human beings from the viewpoint of materialism, you do not come to the idea of freedom. You come to causal conditioning. If you study human beings from a spiritual viewpoint, you come to the determination of the will by God or by spiritual beings; you do not come to free will. You can be a blockhead of a materialist and deny freedom and do research on the natural causality of the will. Or you can be a sophisticated person like Leibnitz and gaze out at a spiritual universe — and you come to determinism. Naturally, as long as you are considering the scale at this left end of the beam, you have to reckon with movement; so long as you are considering the scale at this right end of the beam, again you have to reckon with movement. And it is the same with human beings: whether you consider them from the point of view of nature or from the point of view of spirit, you do not come to freedom. Freedom lies in the middle at the point of balance between them.

That's theory, of course! In practice you have to decide when people come to you with difficult life situations whether you can make them responsible for their actions. Now this becomes a practical question: whether they can or cannot exercise free will. How are you going to decide this? You decide by judging whether their spiritual and physical constitutions are in balance. And in this the physicians and the priests are equally involved. Therefore both physicians and priests must be trained to understand the conditions under which a person is either in balance or not in balance between spirit and nature.

Whether an individual has this sense of responsibility can only be decided out of a deep knowledge of human nature. The problem of freedom in connection with responsibility is one of the deepest imaginable. We will see what from one side leads to health and from the other side leads to pathological conditions.

LECTURE 4

I WOULD LIKE TO INSERT INTO OUR STUDIES a chapter of Anthroposophy that we need for our examination of healthy responsibility and pathological irresponsibility as the physician and the priest must know them.

First of all it is important that we look into the question: what is really inherited by a human being? What is not inherited and must come to the human being in some other way? In evaluating healthy and sick individuals, a great deal depends upon whether one can differentiate between these two ingredients. Human beings come out of the spiritual, supersensible worlds into the sense world: that means, they combine what is given them by heredity with what they bring from earlier earth lives and from life between death and the new birth. Then we see how they develop as a children, from day to day, from week to week. But if one does not perceive that they are four-membered beings, with physical body, etheric body, astral body, and ego organization, one is not in a position to understand their development, for one does not see what part each member is playing in this development. They have different origins; they come from different worlds.

First, human beings have their physical organism. The most striking phenomenon in the physical organism is that in the first period of life they have what we call "first teeth," which last until the time we call "change of teeth." The teeth are only the most obvious thing that is changed at this time. For the fact is that human beings only keep the physical substance they received at birth until the change of teeth. They are constantly stripping that physical material from their form.

The process is, of course, more complicated than is implied in the brief statement that in the course of every seven or eight years a person pushes off all physical substance and replaces it. The truth is near to that, but one need only look at the change of teeth itself to realize that this picture must be modified somewhat. For if this abstract assertion were correct, we would have new teeth every seven years. We get new teeth only once. The teeth are changed once and do not undergo any other renewal. They belong in this category in the most extreme sense. As a matter of fact, the course of human life is such that the older one becomes, the more one retains of old physical substance. A replacement of by far the greatest part of the substance does indeed take place in seven- to eight-year periods; but we must distinguish what remains behind. At the seventh year it is only the adult teeth that remain. After each subsequent period there remain also certain parts of the substance that are not replaced, although the greater part is indeed replaced in the course of seven or eight years. Thus a basic statement can be made for the first seven years. Human beings strip away all the physical substance they had when they were born, keeping none of it, keeping only the forces that have lived and worked in it during those years. These forces have so appropriated the fresh new substance that was constantly being aquired that at seven the physical body has been completely renewed, even to the teeth. And from that statement the understanding must follow that the principle of heredity as our current natural science conceives of it really holds good only for the first seven years of life. Only for those first seven years is it true that a person's characteristics come from parents and grandparents. The physical body of those first seven years provides, in a certain sense, a kind of model from which the artist working in the human being (who consists now in these years of etheric body, astral body, and ego) fashions a new physical body. We see how what we bring down from spiritual worlds — our individuality, our own being — and what we receive from heredity work together in artistic reciprocal activity. If a human being is an inwardly strong individual and brings an intensely strong inner astrality and ego nature, which in turn makes the etheric body strong, then we will see a young person shooting up who

from inner strength keeps very little to the model, only copies it
for the general form. Naturally, the universal human model
must be preserved, and therefore an affinity is already there for
the inherited human form; features of it definitely remain
beyond the change of teeth. Still, to thoughtful observation it
will be apparent that in the case of inwardly strong individuals
important changes come after the change of teeth because such
individuals follow only slightly the model they inherited.

If we investigate such an individual as St. Teresa, we find
that these particularly strong individualities resemble their parents very closely in the first seven years, but then in the ninth
and tenth years they develop in surprising ways. Then the real
individual is emerging. In the strongest sense of the word,
heredity only holds good for the first life period. What seems to
appear later as heredity is not really heredity but must be recognized as a copy of the inherited model. The copy may be more
or less exact; even so, it is not heredity; it is a copy of the inherited characteristics. The ordinary natural scientist considers this
to be simply the principle of heredity carried further. But someone who really studies the nature of humanity will perceive that
there is a complete qualitative difference between the resemblance to parents before the change of teeth and the resemblance
after the change of teeth. Before, the forces of heredity are
active. After, the forces that copy the model are active. To be
exact, one can no more say that a human being has inherited
what is carried between change of teeth and puberty than one
can say of an artist copying the Sistine Madonna in the Dresden
Gallery that the painting has caught the qualities of the Madonna through heredity!

You can see the particular kind of work the etheric body has
to do. For in the years up to the change of teeth, the astral body
and ego organization participate very little. The etheric body
forms a new physical human body in accordance with the
model. Why? Because, like the child during the first seven
years, it is not yet able to receive other than a very special kind
of impression from the outer world. Here we come upon an

important secret of human evolution, a secret that answers the question: What does a child really perceive? The answer lies far away from present-day ideas.

We live, shall we say, between death and a new birth (or conception) in the spiritual world. In the spiritual world we are surrounded by realities very different from those found here in the physical world. We come out of that world into the physical world and continue our life in a physical body that we receive. Now in this physical world the same forces work further, although they are hidden from human sense perception. If you look at a tree, the same spiritual forces are working in it as those you encounter between death and new birth, only they are covered over, veiled, by the physical material of the tree. Everywhere in the physical world in which we live between birth and death, spiritual forces are active behind the sense-perceptible physical entities. We can think of the activities of the spiritual world continuing into this world in which we live between birth and death.

Now in the first seven years of life the child's whole being cannot unite with anything except this spiritual reality in all the colors, all the forms, all warmth, all cold. The child is fully aware when entering this physical world of the continuing spiritual activity. This awareness gradually diminishes up to the change of teeth. A sense impression is quite different to a child than to an adult. This fact is never recognized. To a child the sense impression is something entirely spiritual. For this reason if a child's father has a fit of anger, the child is not conscious of the angry gestures but of the moral state behind the gestures. It is this that passes into the child's body. During this time, therefore, the child is working with the forces that build a physical body in accordance with the child's own model — the body that will now be the child's own — and during this time is turned entirely toward spiritual foundations and works out of spiritual forces.

What does that mean? What is really working when spiritual forces are working? Obviously colors, forms, warmth, cold, roughness, smoothness work upon the sense perceptions. But behind all that, what is the fundamental force that is working? In reality, whatever has to do with an ego nature. Only invisible spiritual beings make an impression on the child, beings who have something to do with an ego nature, above all, beings of the spiritual hierarchies higher than human beings, but also the animal group-souls, and the group-souls of the elemental beings. In reality, all this is working upon the child. And out of these spiritual forces, out of these mighty spiritual dynamics the child forms a second body from the original model. It grows and is finally present as a complete second body when the change of teeth takes place. This is the body that the human being has built for itself since birth, the first body that is it's very own, a physical body built out of the spiritual world.

Thus we have in this first life period very special laws working within all that activates the child, in all the awkwardness and uncertainty that are in the soul and with which it moves. They come from the fact that constant adjustment is having to be made to the physical world, since the child is still dreamily and half-consciously immersed in the other surrounding world: the spiritual world. Someday when medicine reaches a proper spiritual outlook, this interplay between the spiritual and physical worlds during the first seven years of life will be seen as the true cause of the so-called "children's diseases." Then we will have the explanation for a problem that today is solved in the medical books by empty words and formal elucidations that do not lead to any reality.

The etheric body has a great deal to do in these first seven years of life. It works quietly and steadily to develop the faculties that it will possess in the second seven-year period: independent faculties of memory leading toward the intellect. Whoever has an eye for it can see the greatest transformation in the child's soul-life when the first life period goes over into the second. The etheric body is now relieved of the work it had to accomplish — in the full sense of the word — to build the second body. It is relieved, freed. How it is freed, one can only realize if one perceives that at fourteen years not only the teeth remain but still more that had to be renewed, like the teeth, in the first life period. This now remains in the physical-material substance. What remains frees the etheric body — itself becomes free in the etheric body. Quantitatively it is a small thing, but qualitatively it is something of tremendous importance. It is what now becomes tremendously active as soul attributes, soul characteristics. What the human being saves by not having to create a third set of teeth (and much else that is taken care of by evolution in the same way as the teeth) enables something of the etheric body to be "left over." What flowed during the first seven years into the physical development and is now "left over" from the physical development works now purely in the realm of soul, its nature depending upon the individual. With the faculties upon which you call as a teacher in school, the faculties you train, the child accomplished the great change from milk teeth to second teeth, and much else. With the forces that are saved by not having to form a third set of teeth, the child begins to develop soul faculties. This takes place in the depths of human nature. During the first seven years these soul forces had been entirely embedded in the physical development. We have to comprehend physical development as a soul-spiritual activity just as much as a physical activity. We see a spiritual entity active in the body in the first seven years of the human being, in the fullest sense of the word.

How does this relate to general human evolution? Those forces with which the human soul works in the first seven years of life are in the cosmos; they are sun forces. It is not only physical-etheric rays that stream down from the sun: in those physical-etheric sun rays, forces are streaming down from the sun that are identical with the forces by which our etheric body renews our physical body in the first seven years of life. It is the Sun Being (*Sonnenentität*) that works there. Look at the child — how the child works at a second physical body, copying from the model! The child is absorbing pure forces from the sunshine. One must understand that — how humanity stands within the cosmos! And when the child has certain etheric forces released at the change of teeth, they then work back upon the astral organization and ego organization. Then in the second life period human beings have access to what could not reach them at all in the first period. They now have access to the moon forces. The etheric forces in the first seven years of life are sun forces. At the change of teeth we have access to the moon forces; these are identical with the forces of our astral body. Thus at the change of teeth human beings move from the sun sphere — in which, however, we also still remain, for it remains active in us — into the moon sphere. And now between change of teeth and puberty we work on ourselves with the moon forces. With the moon forces we now build our second own body (the third earthly body), in which not so much is replaced as in the first life period, but even so a great deal. Again forces remain behind, but they are now of an astral nature, and they are now transforming the soul. They were freed from their work on the body when we reached puberty. We have now reached a period in which we manifest certain forces that are now free in the soul, forces that had to work in the physical body between the ages of seven and fourteen.

So we work entirely in the first life period with what comes to us from the sun. And with the school child between change of teeth and puberty, it is sun forces that have now become free for soul activity. That is the great powerful fact we find in human evolution, that if one is educating a child's soul between change of teeth and puberty, one has to do purely with sun forces. The child-soul is so intimately related to what lives in the sunshine! One's heart can rejoice in such knowledge. The knowledge really sheds light on the relation between humanity and cosmos.

Moon forces are active in this second life period in the bodily development; they are not yet freed for the soul-life. They become free at puberty, and then they join the work on the soul. The change that takes place in the soul-life at puberty is caused by the fact that moon forces are now impressing themselves into the soul-life. So what a young person does in all kinds of behavior after the onset of puberty is a working together of sun and moon forces.

Thus we see into the depths of human evolution. We will stay clear of speaking of heredity in the crude sense in which natural science speaks of it. We will look in the opposite direction, to see what lives in the human activity of the child. It is the sun that lives in all the human activity of the child, and in the child's human thinking.

It is the sun that streams to us from the stone — for a stone has no light of its own, it can only reflect the sun's light to us. The natural researcher grants you that fact — but that is the very smallest, the most abstract detail! The child also reflects the sun forces back to us, between the seventh and fourteenth years. Just as we can designate the light reflected from the stone as sunlight streamed back to us, so we can designate what the child does in the second life period as "sun." Sun is not merely there where it seems to be concentrated. This physical notion, that the sun is only *there* is like the notion of someone who looks at the soup in a soup bowl and sees a blob of fat floating on the top of it and thinks that the blob of fat is the soup.

Yes, our physical ideas are often very childish, and if one uncovers them and shows them for what they are, then people laugh. One could wish there were the same reaction to much that is happening today in the name of science, because it is pretty laughable. When someone takes the blob of fat to be the soup itself, that's the same as when that gold ball up there above us is regarded as the entire sun. In reality the sun fills the whole world.

Now let us look into the connection between the moon forces and the forces of reproduction. The forces of reproduction now gradually form the child's own second body that is built up between the seventh and fourteenth years and is finished when puberty begins. The human being takes in the reproductive forces during this time; this is plainly moon activity. These forces relate entirely to moon activity. They are the result of moon activity.

And now we reach the life period in which we must form our own third body (the fourth when counted from an external view), the time from puberty to the beginning of the twenties. The division of time in the later years is no longer so exact as the time between change of teeth and puberty. Now there is always more physical substance remaining behind; it stays fixed in the human being, it becomes permanent structure. Gradually a great deal of permanent structure accumulates. The older a person becomes, the less material is stripped away from the bones and replaced. Also in the rest of the organism certain parts need a longer time to separate off. And one can see a simple fact in connection with the teeth: that once one has got one's second set of teeth, whether one still has them later depends upon how long they last — just as with a knife, one only has it as long as it lasts. The knife can't renew itself. Teeth can't renew themselves either, really.

Obviously everything is in flow: there is renewal in the first place, but then it goes over into the state of nonrenewal. The teeth maintain their life process at a much slower tempo than the rest of the organism, so far as intensity is concerned. But therefore in reverse, the tempo is faster so far as quality is concerned, for they actually become bad before the other parts of the organism — for the reason that the other parts can always renew themselves. If the teeth were subject to the same laws as many other parts of the human organism, there wouldn't have to be any dentists. On the other hand, if the other parts of the organism were subject to the same laws as the teeth, we would all die young in this modern civilization of ours.

But now to go on. We are active in our organism in the first seven years of life with the forces of the sun, in the second seven years with the forces of the moon. In this second period the sun forces remain and the moon forces combine with them. In the third seven-year period, from puberty into the twenties, much more delicate forces are taken in, coming from the other planets. These other planetary forces appear in the human growth process, and because they work much less strongly than the sun or moon, their influence is outwardly much less visible. They had been working in the body between the fourteenth and the twenty-first years. Now at twenty-one, although it is hardly noticeable, they begin to work in the area of soul and spirit. Whoever has insight can see this remarkable change. Up to that moment only sun and moon have spoken out of human deeds. Now planetary forces modify that sun and moon activity. Actually people's coarse methods of observation afford very little capacity for grasping this change. But it is there.

Knowledge of these connections is necessary for someone concerned with the human being in health and in illness. For what do we really know of a human being, shall we say in the eleventh or twelfth year, if we don't know that the moon forces are working there? After that period, even though there are continually fewer parts to be renewed, the person must still renew them. Up to the twenty-first or twenty-second year, the sun, moon, and planets are working in succession into human growth. Then from the twenty-first to the twenty-eighth year the constellations of the fixed stars work. To be sure, this escapes ordinary observation. Only mystery wisdom tells of the entire zodiac playing into the human being between the beginning and the end of the twenties. Then the world becomes severe. It no longer wants to work into a person; it becomes harsh. Of this strange new relation of the human being to the world in the twenty-eighth, twenty-ninth year — that the world hardens toward us — of this, today's science hardly knows anything. Aristotle taught it to Alexander when he told him that we push against the crystal heaven and find it hard. Thus "the crystal heaven," beyond the sphere of the fixed stars, acquires meaning for human comprehension. And one begins to realize that when we come to the end of our twenties, we find no more forces in the cosmos for our own renewal. Why do we not die, then, at twenty-eight years? Well, the surrounding world does in fact let us die at twenty-eight. It is true. Whoever sees humanity's relation to the world, whoever looks consciously out into the world, must say, "O world, in reality you sustain me only until my twenty-eighth year!" Only when one realizes this does one finally begin to understand the real nature of the human being.

For now what happens when the world withdraws its formative forces — forces that previously we had always been free to use to build ourself up? At this remarkable moment, when in the twenty-eighth year we begin to show clearly that the earlier forces of growth are now completely gone, some people begin to die off. Some hold on a little longer to the forces of growth that are flowing away. But even Goethe had grown smaller when he measured himself carefully. This was when he began to work again on the second part of *Faust*. Earlier he had already begun to fade. From the moment when the world deserts us, we have to manage our renewal ourselves, out of forces we have received up to that moment. Certainly when the parts of our organism that can be renewed are becoming fewer and fewer, we cannot work to give ourselves a new body in the same glorious measure that children use up to the change of teeth, when they are forming their first very own body from the model. But we have collected many, many forces from sun and moon and stars which we are carrying within us and which we need when at twenty-eight we have to begin to renew our physical-material body ourselves. This is the moment in earth-life when we find that we are now given complete responsibility for our human form. This moment of our life when we are put entirely on our own is the point of time toward which we have been striving, and from which we must go on. We strive from childhood when we are receiving many cosmic forces, strive more and more toward a point lying at the end of our twenties, when we no longer build our growth out of cosmic forces. Whatever we do after that moment, we do from forces out of our own body. In the middle is the point at which we stop working with cosmic forces and begin to develop forces out of our own body.

We often find a premature activity happening in some child from forces out of the child's own body. We become aware of it from certain pathological symptoms the child shows from the bones, for instance, becoming brittle, and particularly from becoming fat. But the connection between these things is not easily seen. In every moment of life a person is either striving toward this twenty-eighth-year point or away from it. You must realize that it is a kind of zero point, a kind of hypomochlion, a zero moment in time when we stand between ourselves and the world. Always in our inner dynamics we are striving toward it or from it. Whatever is happening in us is a striving toward a zero or away from a zero, something we do toward or away from nothingness. We are striving toward the point where the world is no longer active and we are not yet active. Between the two conditions is a kind of zero. There is something in us that is oriented toward nothingness. It is this that makes us free beings; that is why we can hold responsibility. It is rooted in the human constitution that we are responsible free beings, because at the moment of transfer from the world to ourselves we go through a point of zero. Just as the beam of a pair of scales goes through a point of zero from right to left, from left to right, and that point does not follow the laws to which the rest of the scales is subject. You can think when you have a pair of scales, *here* the mechanical laws you have learned are in force; this gives the scales an exact form — either this above and that below or the opposite. That is the law of scales, the law of leverage. You can carry the scales around; their relation remains the same everywhere, subject always to those mechanical laws wherever you take them — except at this point. This point is free. You can carry the point around as if it were not connected to a pair of scales: the scales remain unchanged. And so it is, when you take hold of yourself in your soul experiences at that point toward which first you strive, from which afterward you strive away: first the world is active, afterward you yourself, and *here* nothing is active. With the tendency toward and the tendency from, here where a hypomochlion sits, here can live freely that human capacity which is determined neither by nature nor by the world. Here is the point of origin of human freedom. Here is where responsibility is born.

If, therefore, one wants to be able to judge the degree of responsibility in, for instance, a person thirty-five years old — and I mean professionally, not merely a layman's opinion, or that of a dilettante — then one must ask oneself, has too much, perhaps, worked over from this person's abnormal development up to the point at the end of the twenties? Is the point moved more toward youth or more toward age? A person is properly responsible if the point is normal, if judging the whole individual from external life one can decide that the point is normal. If it lies too far back toward youth — that is, if the world ceased too soon to give its forces to some person — one may perhaps find that the person suffers easily, even though to a small degree, from compulsive ideas. The soul is becoming rigid and cannot be held fully accountable for its deeds.

If the point comes late, the question will be whether that person is hindered by his or her inner nature from developing complete freedom of soul and is too rigid physically, and for that reason cannot be held fully responsible. The physician and the priest are the ones who are competent to form this judgment, in the finest sense of the word. They will know that they can judge pretty accurately from people's appearance what their development has been, whether they are in balance, whether their life-hypomochlion is at the right spot, that is, at the right point of time, or is too early or too late. We will discuss physical appearance later, for even an intensive study of physiognomy belongs to pastoral medicine.

These are things that in the old mystery wisdom were regarded as very important for judgments of human life. They are things that have been forgotten and that must be brought again into our knowledge of the human being if that knowledge is to have any beneficial influence, if it is to be active in the right sense in medical and pastoral activity.

LECTURE 5

WE HAVE NOW GAINED KNOWLEDGE in one direction, of individuals who, although not exactly having intuition, do develop a perception of the spiritual world and who show certain aspects of behavior that to a physician may seem to be pathological but are in fact something quite different, something more. For as you have seen, the pathological condition remains with them *in statu nascendi* and there is continuous healing coming from the spirit. This is the case with such personalities as St. Teresa and Mechthild of Magdeburg,[5] as well as with male visionaries.

When we study these individuals, we find that as a first stage the ego organization separates from the rest of the human organism. It then draws the astral body closely to it, in a certain sense away from the physical-etheric organism. This is in the waking state. What is the consequence of this? You can easily see that this puts the individual into a kind of dream condition. From a spiritual-scientific point of view the ego, by drawing the astral body to itself, is not allowing it to enter the physical and etheric bodies completely, and this brings about a kind of dream condition. But because of the special karmic density, both ego and astral body are strong, and they bring into the dream condition receptivity for the perception of the spiritual world. Dream is transformed into a state in which the individual is really able to see into the spiritual world and to feel the presence of spiritual beings.

Now let us look at the extreme opposite condition. Here the ego is weak, and the astral body draws it down too strongly into the rest of the organism — again in the waking state. Then there is not illumination, as with visionaries like St. Teresa, but the opposite: a darkening, a clouding, a lowering of consciousness — in the waking state — to a dream condition.

One cannot learn to know this second type of person in the

way I have indicated for the first type. Individuals who feel the presence of spiritual beings, who come to such final stages as St. Teresa or Mechthild of Magdeburg, are much more numerous than one would think. One learns to know them if one has some particular opportunity or if one has cultivated the corresponding faculties. One learns to know them best by letting them tell about their conditions. They talk more interestingly than our ordinary contemporaries. Their narratives are much more interesting; above all, they speak of things one does not encounter in everyday life. So they are already interesting in the first stage.

The opposite individuals, those whose astral body is drawing the ego down, are also interesting if one lets them talk about themselves. To understand the first type of person requires the soul depth of the priest. To understand this second type of person — who often is even more interesting than the usual visionaries, who do not develop very far — really requires the sensitivity of a physician who comprehends the world with a good intelligence and a fair amount of intuition. For it is a matter of understanding what they do *not* tell one: what they do tell one is of little value. It is a matter of grasping what they say or do in such a way that one can think of it in relation to the human organism. Such persons, if one asks them a question, show a certain amount of stupidity, also unwillingness to answer a question. They begin to talk about something quite foreign to what one is asking. But if one catches hold of what they say about themselves — and some of them talk endlessly — one sometimes has the feeling that they possess an inner source of speech that gives them a special association of ideas such as the ordinary person does not have. They'll tell you if you let them ramble on — you mustn't ask questions, you must just snap up what they tell as it were by chance — For example a man might say: "Sure, ten years ago I was in a farmer's house and the wife gave me some coffee. The cup had red roses painted on it. She couldn't give me the coffee right away because she'd forgotten the sugar was in the kitchen and she had to go and get it. And she forgot the milk. She had to get the milk from down in the cellar. And then she poured almost half a cup of milk into the coffee. And she said, 'My coffee is very good.' And I said, 'Yes, I think so too, farmer lady.'" And so he goes on and on. He tells incidents from far in his past, and goes into the most unbelievable details. You think, "If I only had a memory as good as his!" — forgetting that if you did have as good a memory you would be just like him! Now of course I'm telling it this way to portray a type, and to show a typical outcome. You must then think of the corresponding lighter variations that you meet in life, which the physician especially meets. I'm picturing an extreme case so that you can see the chief characteristics.

So when the astral body draws the ego organization in, there comes about a kind of power for reproducing details of memory as though automatically. It is always ready to repeat them; it is indifferent to logical connections and just tells things one after another. As a result one can't help wondering why the person hits upon one thing at one moment and another thing at the next. His tale can go on like this, for instance: "The farmer lady went to get the milk and while she was gone I looked in the corner of the room and there was a Madonna picture and it was the same one I'd seen thirty years earlier in another place but there I didn't have coffee but a very good soup." It can happen that he comes entirely away from the first part of his narrative, but it can also happen that he returns to it again. One sees that this is not a logical memory but a space-and-time memory, extraordinarily exact, with a compulsive desire to tell everything. It is a memory in which, when one studies it more closely, one sees something very remarkable — one sees its deeper foundation. One notices that the person enjoys the sound of certain words he had associated with certain events while he was experiencing the events themselves, and now he takes pleasure in sounding these words again. He is in fact going back to speech that was kept in his memory while thoughts were pushed out — not completely, but almost so.

One also notices changes in the sphere of the will. To these one must pay attention, for now the beginning of real

pathological conditions can be found. One will encounter the
following — again, one must pay attention, for nothing much
can be acclomplished if, for instance, one approaches such people to do this or that in order to observe them. For they become
amazingly stubborn, they don't want to cooperate, won't answer
questions, won't do anything. But if one can obtain an earlier
case history and put those things together with what can be
learned from the person's neighbors or a similar source, then one
discovers, for instance, that such a person feels a terrific impulse
at a definite time of the year to go wandering off somewhere.
Often it is to the same region each year. And this inner impulse
of will works so strongly that if one tries at such a moment to
counteract it, just to discover what state the person is in, one
can, for instance, notice the following.

Take a gourmand (there are gourmands even among such
people as these!). Catch up with him while he is wandering
and sit him down to a wonderful meal or two — to what gives
him his greatest joy in life. You'll find that he will only stay put
the first day, possibly a second day if he is still a good distance
from the place he is heading for. He becomes restless, for he
would love another fine meal, and he knows that the next place
he'll reach has frightful food. He knows that, for his memory
is unusually well developed. He becomes anxious. He wants to
go on, for he cannot adapt his will to sudden external suggestions. Just as on the one hand he cannot adapt himself to
immediate sense impressions but brings out every possible gem
from his speech coffers, so on the other hand he cannot adapt
himself to the necessity of surrendering his will-limb system to
life's external circumstances. He wants just to follow his own
will-impulses, which drive him from within in a very definite
manner. One sees that he has almost completely lost the faculty of the ego organization that unites a human being with the
outer world. His senses are dulled; his will-impulses prevent
him from having a normal relation to the world, and he wants
only to follow these will-impulses. This is the consequence of
the ego being drawn down into the astral body.

So you see, such people could be helped very much if our medical understanding and the loving devotion of the theologians would work together — not, however, by some instant therapy, but in the following way. With these people one can observe a very definite situation. First we have to consider their life between the change of teeth and puberty. In that period, from a superficial point of view usually nothing abnormal is to be noticed. Everyone loves to see how clever these children are, how frightfully clever, what clever answers they can give, "just like an adult!" But one should be alert to this clever answering between the seventh and the fourteenth year. The children who are so excessively clever at this age are receiving something in this period before puberty that they should only have for their development *after* puberty. That is how the condition that I have just been describing comes about. The astral body should only be drawing the ego down after puberty, so that then the ego can completely unfold by the beginning of the twenties. With these children the astral body has already drawn the ego down after the change of teeth or in the ninth, tenth, eleventh year. We observe the abnormal cleverness and are delighted by it. By the time the late teens come, the eighteenth, nineteenth, twentieth years, the ego is stuck too deeply in the astral body. Then the condition is present that I have described, along with the symptoms that I indicated. So now if a child worries us in those early years by premature cleverness, it is a matter of giving certain kinds of treatment. First of all, there will be situations where physician and priest will have to confer with the teacher, so that the teacher will realize what should be done for that early life period. When we have finished this general characterization, we will make several detailed suggestions of what can actually be done. But first I'd like to carry this further, to indicate certain clear connections between the various themes we've been discussing.

Now the following can happen: the etheric body on its part can draw the astral body and ego in too strongly, so that they snap to an excessive degree into the physical and etheric bodies — again in the waking state. Then we have the situation that, seen from within, there is too much astrality in the organs; it cannot unite properly with them. This condition is the pathological mirror-picture of a visionary state such as, for instance, that of St. Teresa, such as her "first stage" as I described it, when she felt the presence of spiritual beings. We had there the bringing of waking-sleep into clear consciousness. And now in such persons as I am describing we have the opposite: dreams are carried over into waking life, with the accompanying symptoms I have mentioned. For it really happens in waking life: dreams do not appear, but an active "dream" life that discloses itself in the kind of speech I described, and in that extreme turning inward of the will impulses. That is the pathological mirror-picture of ordinary dreaming. Activity is there instead of the passivity that is the normal condition of dreaming.

Then we have the second stage, the drawing down of the ego and astral organization by the etheric body. The individual snaps too strongly with the ego, astral body, and etheric body into the physical organism, and the physical organism is not able to receive them into its single organs. Every possible organ has excess astrality that could not unite properly with the organ. Now we have the pathological mirror-picture of what we learned was the second stage for the individuals in whom sense impressions were in a certain sense stimulated from within. The direction was from within out to the senses. Now in this mirror-picture the direction is the opposite: it goes inward to the organs, it takes hold of the physical organism. And conditions appear that always appear when a physical or etheric organ is flooded by the astral body and ego organization and they cannot unite so that it could be called a proper saturation of the physical body by the etheric and astral bodies. Something is left over in the physical organs from the higher members of the organism. What in the other type of individuals poured into visions similar to a sense perception, with colors like a sense perception, visions that revealed the spiritual world, is in this case pouring itself inward, wanting to seize a physical organ. In the former situation there was a reaching out more externally, to the spiritual world beyond the sense world. In this case there is a reaching inward to a physical organ, manifesting in so-called "seizures," all the different forms of real epilepsy or epileptoid symptoms ("temporal lobe seizures"). It can be explained as the snapping down of the ego and astral organization too strongly into the physical organism, which then succeeds in drawing the etheric body to itself. We see how the first condition advances to this second condition.

Hereby we see something in modern life that could be prevented if a real pastoral medicine would come about. People do not realize that the first condition is pathological; they simply find it interesting. And they only become aware of the second condition when seizures or other epileptic symptoms appear. The memory is now no longer expanding into detail, and the inner will-impulses are no longer increasing: now, since the astral and ego organizations are being pulled inward, and therefore the astral organization is failing to relate properly to certain organs, we find the memory is extinguished. Instead of the memory clinging to details as in the previous condition (details with no logical relation, that were just a running stream of unassociated pictures), now we find the memory disrupted, collapsed, a memory with gaps in it. This can become so extreme that the person lives in a kind of double consciousness. For instance, the memory clings to the upper organs — for the whole human being participates in memory — it takes hold of the upper organs, deserting the lower organs. Then this is reversed: the upper organs lose the memory activity and the lower organs receive it again. There is a rhythmic alteration. Such things can happen. And so these people have two streams of consciousness flowing parallel to each other. In one stream they remember everything that occurs when they are in the one condition; in the other stream they remember all the other things. And they never know in one condition of consciousness any of the content of the other condition of consciousness. Thus the memory deteriorates to a pathological level.

There we have the pathological mirror-picture of what we found in the second stage of the saint. Let us use that term, for modern medicine has no word for such a thing. Saints have a world around them that is visionary but that has a spiritual content. They reach into the spiritual world and receive inner impressions of it. People with pathological conditions — because their karma has given them a weak personality — are drawn down into the physical body. Instead of receiving visions of spiritual things they have epileptic conditions, empty gaps in consciousness, a lack of coherence in daily waking life, and so forth.

But now there can be still a third stage. This is the stage at which for karmic reasons the physical body has become even weaker, along with all the other members, so that earlier karmic forces no longer operate sufficiently in the physical body. With such a person it now comes about, not that ego, astral, and etheric body are pulled in by the physical body, but that something quite different happens. I shall have to describe it in the following way.

Think how it is with those who are extremely sensitive in the other direction, in the direction of the senses, that is, in the direction of the ego organization. How painfully sensitive they can be to all that flows in through the senses, to strong colors, lively sounds. Now precisely the opposite is the case with those whose physical body is weak from karmic causes. Such people are not hypersensitive from within outward, but are insensitive to their physical body and yield to an excessive degree to everything from the other side, the side of the will, that is, from the outer physical world. They succumb to heaviness, warmth, cold. All of this affects them not as it normally affects organic beings, but as it affects inorganic things. This then stifles the expression of the astral body and ego. They are hemmed in by the world and because of a weak physical body they cannot confront it with the necessary intensity; they are like a piece of the outer world although they are still inside their physical body. This is clearly the exact opposite of what we described as the third stage for the saint. The saint goes through pain that is then transformed into bliss, and then further to an experience of the spiritual world in its pure spirituality. This is called "rest in God" or "rest in the Spirit."

But people who develop in the way I am now describing do not come to "rest in God" or "rest in the Spirit." They come, although they are not conscious of it, to rest in the hidden occult forces of the physical world, forces against which they, as human beings, should actually be maintaining their independence. They develop the pathological mirror-picture of the third stage of the saint: the condition called idiocy, in which the human personality is lost, in which a person rests in outer nature, that is, in the hidden forces of nature. They can no longer manifest as a human being. They live only in the natural processes that go on within them, in what is a continuation of external natural processes, vegetable processes — eating food, digesting food, moving about in whatever way digestion and the food substances give an impulse to move. It is a complete waking sleep given over to the bodily functions, which are not under the control of the weak physical body but are active as processes in the outer world are active. Naturally, since these processes are working in a human being they do give human-like impulses. But these people are isolated from the normal human world because they are pushed into the physical world to too great a degree. Here we have to do with everything that is a pathological mirror-picture of the "rest in God." We can call it "rest in Nature." It has to do with the various paranoid states, with what in everyday life is called idiocy, while the previous conditions would be called mental retardation.

So we have seen the progression in the case of the saint from feeling the presence of spiritual beings to a third stage, being present in the spiritual world. And we have seen the opposite pathological states: first, psychopathological impairment as the first stage. We can be particularly aware of this stage when we encounter an abnormal wanderlust, as I described, connected with a memory that lacks logic. We see this progress to states of insanity, of which the early stage will still allow a person to pursue certain activities in external life. Then we see this progress to the third stage — which could also have been present in early childhood *in statu nascendi.* The second stage can be due to the fact that no one has been able to recognize and counteract certain conditions in the first life period, between birth and change of teeth. Occasionally young children show, not exactly an excessive cleverness, but rather an unusual desire to learn things — something that should only appear after the change of teeth. This characteristic is normal between change of teeth and puberty. When it appears in the first life period, however, we should be concerned and we should find the means — physical, soul, and spiritual means — to cure what is already pathological. It is of utmost importance to investigate how certain capacities can be prevented from shining down into the first seven years of life that should really only emerge during the second seven years.

The third stage can reveal itself in two ways. In most cases a person brings it along as his or her karma — as you have seen from my descriptions. Already at birth, the person is in an abnormal condition because of some unusual stress in putting together the etheric body before entering the physical body. An etheric body was formed that does not want to penetrate the physical body completely, does not want to enter heart and stomach in the proper way but wants to flood them: in other words, an etheric body that carries the astral body and ego organization too strongly into the various organs. Already at birth or very soon after, we see facial or bodily deformities that can give us deep concern. This is called congenital mental retardation — but there is no such thing! There is only karmic mental retardation, related to the child's entire destiny. We will also speak about this more fully, so that you will see how an incarnation spent in such mental dullness can, under certain conditions, even have a beneficial place in a human being's karma, although it may mean misery in that one incarnation. There is need, after all, to regard things not merely from the point of view of finite life, but *sub specie aeterni* from the point of view of the immortal life of a human being. Then we would have a compassionate charity *(caritas)* and a wise one as well.

On the other hand, the second stage I have described can progress to the third stage in the following way. If in the first life period, between birth and change of teeth, not only the second life period shines in but also the third — the period between puberty and the twenties, when our organization should work into our organism — then we see a child in their fourth or fifth year with capacities that often delight the people. They say, "This child talks or acts like a twenty-year-old!" But this is what is happening: the ego organization is developing too early and is overpowering the physical body and making it weak. Idiocy will then appear in the latter part of the person's life. In this case it is not brought on by karma but has been acquired in this very life, and can only be balanced out karmically in later lives. If we observe life intelligently and have a good pastoral medicine to support us, we will be able to prevent it simply by providing the proper education for such a person's early childhood.

Whoever is vocationally drawn to observe such things should do so not only as individual symptoms — where, naturally, they should be studied with special love — but should also cultivate an understanding for them as a general phenomenon. Such a person should also develop an understanding for how these things are brought about.

We have seen how much of the pedagogy of former decades that a healthy pedagogy, such as the Waldorf school pedagogy wants to be, must definitely oppose. Yet these things have become extraordinarily precious to people. Sometimes our Waldorf school education must address certain things with tremendous severity, for instance, the Froebel kindergarten work, which is taken not from life but out of the intellect. Before the change of teeth it occupies children with activities that are not an imitation of life but are invented out of people's heads. This is putting into the child's first years of life something that should not be there until the next period, between change of teeth and puberty. This brings on the first stage of a pathological condition, a mild state of illness that often is not yet regarded as pathological. Also it were better, perhaps, not to label it pathological, otherwise so much else would have to be labeled pathological, which must in any case be recognized as "cultural phenomena." These things cannot merely be criticized, they must be understood, so that one relates to them in the right way.

What we should see in front of us is wrong education in early childhood. The second life period has been carried into the first. This is the underlying cause creating a person's automatic speech and stirring the will from within outwards without adjusting in any degree to the surrounding world. Think of a situation such as I described as the first pathological stage: a slight tendency, caused by bad education, education going the wrong way. Then what happens? Wanderlust. This impulse is not entirely pathological, but it is characterized by the desire at a certain age to follow none but one's own ideas, not to bother about the world, to get free and away from one's surroundings, to wander at will! It is connected with other contemporary phenomena that also have their origin in a pathological education, or at least an education with a pathological tinge. You can observe this right now. Look at some of these youth groups. Their very existence belongs to the lifestyle of the last decades of the Kali Yuga.[6] There is an affinity between this slightly pathological condition and the kind of life that the Kali Yuga brought about. These things all belong together. But they must be examined from these two aspects. If you look, you will easily see tinges of what I have been describing. They reveal themselves clearly in wanderlust, but that is an extreme symptom. Listen once in a while to their conversations! One despairs at their indifference to what one says to them. They repeat details eternally, details they describe as their "experience"; they come back again and again to the same thing.

Please don't misunderstand me! I'm certainly not pointing to any of these things in a trivial sense. My intention is to show you that such phenomena can only be really understood if one grasps clearly the connection I've been pointing to during these few days: that there is always a step into spiritual life and its extreme opposite — a step into the physical body. A further step into the spiritual world for the saint; a further step into the body, into seizures, for instance, for the psychopath. And so on. That is the relationship. If you consider how in the external world, in electricity and magnetism, one pole is always dependent upon the other, you will realize that in life too there can be such a relation between two poles of human development.

This, of course, cannot be seized upon clumsily, as happens today so often with the materialistic worldview. This fact, that there are polar opposites here and that there is a connection between the two poles, must be approached with delicacy. Then one will begin to see what can develop in the one and the other direction. One will finally learn in this way to see into the nature of the human being.

LECTURE 6

SEPTEMBER 13, 1924

SO FAR WE HAVE BEEN CHIEFLY CONCERNED with discovering how far a human being may deviate in one or the other direction from what can be called "normal": toward a pathological condition or toward a connection to the real spiritual world. With the help of a rather obvious example, I would like to go beyond the single earth-life to show how the karma that a human being carries through repeated earth-lives must sometimes relate itself to entirely contrasting conditions, such as, for instance, a capacity to reach into the spiritual world and, in the same human being, a need to reach down into the bodily, natural realm.

If physicians want to practice not only with good external measures and with intelligence but with their whole heart, with all their human capacities, they need to stand within the spiritual world and look at this physical world from a spiritual point of view. The human being journeys through successive earth-lives; causes reach over spiritually from one earth-life and evoke consequences in a later one. Therefore karma cannot remain a mere word to us. We must learn how to relate our healing activity to karma. For this, we must first be fully aware of how karma works in relation to pathological conditions and also to visionary capacities.

If priests want to enter into their parishioners' life situations in the right way, if they want to be a real pastor to the souls in their care, they also need to appreciate the spiritual significance of what confronts a human being in everyday life on this earth. Only then will they be able to care for humanity properly from the standpoint of the spirit.

In this connection we should consider something for a moment that some with a modern, more "enlightened" point of view may regard with derision. If we, too, presumed to take such an attitude, our descendants would surely magnify it a hundred-fold in their estimation of us! For they will view us in future centuries as anyone living today in our so-called scientific culture views our ancestors. You will see at once what I mean.

In the course of human evolution a complete reversal has taken place in the conception of illness. This became particularly obvious at the end of the nineteenth and beginning of the twentieth century. If you go back two thousand years or so to the early times of the Old Testament, you find a universal conviction that illness comes from sinfulness, that illness has its original spiritual cause in sin. This was a serious belief. There had to be a spiritual error or failure somewhere as the true cause when a physical illness appeared. This idea was carried further. It was believed of a person in whom the spiritual fault lay causing the illness, that the individual harbored some elemental spiritual force that did not belong there, that somehow the person was "possessed." In those times all illness signified that a person was "possessed" by some spiritual entity as the consequence of spiritual error or fault. Therapy was created accordingly. It was based on finding the means to bring out of the ill person the alien elemental spirituality that had entered through a spiritual offense. Basically this was the belief: that one does not understand an illness unless one knows its cause.

Now consider the belief that came later, pronouncing exactly the opposite view — before psychoanalysis intervened in such a frightfully dilettantish fashion. The new belief said that every sin can be traced to illness. People were convinced of it. If there was a criminal, a "sinner" somewhere (the concept "sin" was defined rather superficially, according to the legal code) they saw to it that in some way or other they got hold of the brain after death, and could thus examine the physical organism. They were looking for the defects. And they did find defects in many instances. In this respect they have advanced quite a little. Clever, well-trained scientists have adopted the view that a person who has a perfect physical organism doesn't sin. A person sins if there is some bodily defect. Sin comes from disease. That's how evolution goes — not in a straight line but by way of opposites. And the people who have now reached this last view (not everyone today admits to it, but it is often fundamental even for those who do not totally subscribe to it) look back with pity to olden times when it was believed that illness comes from sin. For they know they themselves are right, that sin comes from illness. And they know with absolute certainty that in the sick person there is some material process or other that they have to combat, have to neutralize, have to get out of the organism. In earlier times the healers worked to remove a host of elemental spirits. To someone who sees the matter from a broader point of view there is really not very much difference. From an inner standpoint there is no great difference between the health spas that materialistic medicine considers correct and Lourdes. In the latter a person is cured through religious beliefs, in the former through materialistic beliefs. These things must simply be looked at without prejudice.

Influenced by such shortsighted ideas, one certainly will not perceive real connections. Therefore I would like to describe a concrete case. It should reveal to you the deeper connections to be found in this matter of human health. A certain person lived in the nineteenth century. I'll speak of him presently as he was in the nineteenth century, but first I want to take you back to one of his earlier incarnations that had important consequences for his life in the nineteenth century. This person was incarnated in a southeastern region of Asia where the people were extraordinarily fond of animals. You know that oriental teachings include a great reverence and love for animals; they extend what they call love of humanity and love of things, particularly to love of animals. In ancient times it was natural for people in this region to love animals intensely and to take very good care of them. But the man of whom I am speaking was no friend of animals. There in the midst of an animal-loving people was a man who treated them cruelly. Even as a boy he tormented them, he was mean to them; in later life he tortured domestic animals in every possible way to an incredible degree. This aroused violent anger in the people among whom he lived. He also experienced a deep conflict between this compulsive mania (today, in materialistic terms, we would call it perversion of the will) and on the other hand the spiritual teachings of the people. He took these up with great fervor. He was able to relate himself to them completely; he had a fine sense for everything the religion of that area taught. But he became involved in violent conflicts with the most religious individuals around him because of his torture of animals. It was especially the animals in his own house that he tortured, first among his relatives, and later when he became a kind of farmhand. Orientals lavish particularly good care on domestic animals, considering them as part of the family. These were the ones he tortured most shockingly.

This man lived again in our age, in the first half of the nineteenth century, and in this incarnation (which in a wider sense belongs to our own time) he was born as an extremely fearful person, so that he chained dogs to himself. One could say this was now a symptom of illness, this abnormal relation to animals. It did have an aspect of disease about it through the fact that he did not develop any special love for the dogs, only a feeling that he had to have them near him. It is clearly fantastic, the way he related himself to them. It reveals an inner karmic compulsion from an earlier life.

At the same time in this incarnation the man is extremely talented, carrying over from his earlier life everything he had experienced of the oriental spiritual teachings, as well as his own religious devotion. This is not just a feeling in him: it becomes his life practice. In the course of this life he develops not only an astonishing capacity for spiritual fantasy, but the ability to put into poetic form correct visionary images that come to him in a matter-of-fact way. His poetry is about ordinary physical human life into which elemental spiritual beings constantly play. He is a distinguished poet. Moreover one may truly say he is the dramatist whom we Europeans would compare most seriously with Shakespeare. He is Ferdinand Raimund[7] — with his fantastic personality, his giant talent — whose dramatic poems show how he has brought from earlier incarnations his ability to portray spiritual things, to put spiritual happenings into human life. One need only look at *Der Alpenkönig und der Menschenfeind* ("The King of the Alps and the Misanthrope") to be able to liken him to Shakespeare. First of all, he is an important actor; this comes from his impulse to bring both trivialities and non-trivialities from spiritual realms to the stage. On the stage he is an incomparable actor, full of humor; in life he is completely overwhelmed by the consequences of the animal torture that he formerly perpetrated. Genius and a pathological condition are thoroughly mixed in him: the genius impelling him to create with soul-spiritual dramatic instinct and Shakespearean power, the pathological condition impelling him to inject a fantastic element into his external life.

Now we must look at a singular trait in Raimund. The animal torture had been a "necessity" to him in that earlier incarnation; he experienced a kind of lust, he did it for secret pleasure. During that earth-life he was not aware it was bad. He came to that realization only after he went through the gate of death. Now the experience one has when one goes through the gate of death and then further into the life between death and a new birth is in the subsequent life expressed foremost (in a wide sense) in the head organization. There lies the impulse one brings with one as talent. This, Raimund brought with him in rich amount. But here also something is working that appears in the rhythmic system, particularly the upper rhythmic or respiratory system. For the human being is built like this (see drawing on next page): metabolic-limb system, rhythmic system, nerve-sense system. What comes from an earlier earth-life works over into the nerve-sense system of the new life; what comes from the time between death and a new birth works over into the rhythmic system; and what comes from the new earth-life works alone in the metabolic-limb sytem.

So all that this individual who is now Ferdinand Raimund experienced of bitter remorse, of deeply crushing insight was working continually after that earlier incarnation, in his life

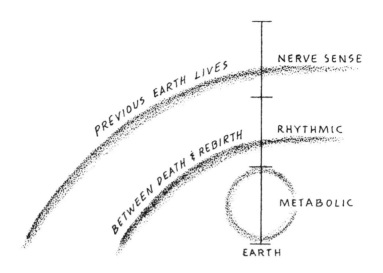

between death and a new birth, affecting his coming rhythmic system. It worked right into the physical body. For in the physical organization of the head we have the after-effect of the previous earth-life; in the physical organization of the rhythmic system we have the after-effect of the life between death and a new birth. These facts are obvious when one studies embryology even externally.

In Raimund's case, in his breathing system, the upper rhythmic system, we see working in him all the bitter remorse and insight he had experienced when he went through the gate of death from that previous earth-life. This experience led inevitably to breathing irregularities in this life, to a meager intake of oxygen and a strong saturation of carbon dioxide. Breathing irregularities — from a physical point of view — bring on a variety of states of anxiety; they can be the carriers of elemental beings of anxiety. The breathing irregularities do not allow the proper balance of oxygen and carbon dioxide in the breathing process, and this draws in anxiety elementals. You can see all this in *The King of the Alps and the Misanthrope*. It was well developed in Raimund; he was predisposed to a breathing system that would be a carrier for anxiety elementals.

Such elemental beings are not simply anxiety elementals. If at the same time there is something such as Raimund had in his head system from earlier earth-lives, namely, soul-spiritual ideas — which make his dramas so interesting — one sees that the presence of these anxiety demons causes karma to develop in a very definite direction. One sees clearly how they push in an unhealthy way to bring about karmic effects. They stream into fanciful imaginations that even achieve visionary content — and Raimund's dramas are built on such content. They stream into his visionary activity; they also impel him to develop a fantastic element in his daily life. In this way a karmic stream pushes through his life, a tremendous gift of genius that has to come to expression. One branch of the stream flows in a special kind of spiritual creation. The other branch flows parallel in a kind of life-fantasy that is not expressed externally but is directed inward. For it lies in the rhythmic system, which is of course half inward, but which also works in the lower organs in such a way that it affects a person's external life, and then in turn influences the inner life again. So Raimund's genius is accompanied by a truly pathological tendency. And this pathological tendency, which expresses itself through the anxiety demons, is the vehicle for the fulfillment of his karma.

One can see Raimund's karma quite clearly. He has to keep a dog. He is a fantastic person. He does what other men wouldn't do. One can understand that. One can even sympathize with that. Indeed when I remember how some of our worthy citizens have gorged themselves at court banquets when they were being given distinguished titles, I have a certain sympathy for Raimund, with his wry humor as he sits on the floor and eats with the dog out of the dog's bowl. You see how karma plays in from the animal torture of his earlier incarnation. You see how this deed comes from the animal torture and the remorse after death and is done as a fantastic atonement. But the atonement has to be still more severe. Immediately after this, the anxiety demons appear and take part in the playing-out of his karma. Raimund becomes obsessed by the thought: the dog has rabies, I have been eating with him, now I am infected! Raimund is terrified. While at other moments he can do the most talented things on the stage, the moment he withdraws from his external life he succumbs to the compulsive fear that he is infected with rabies.

Now he undertakes a journey with a friend. They go from Vienna to Salzburg, and there the fear of madness so overwhelms him that he must return at once to Vienna to get treatment. It is a tormenting journey both for him and for the friend. One sees his pathological state always following at the heels of his genius. For now he is well taken care of: people are delighted to entertain Ferdinand Raimund. Gradually he abandons the rabies idea. Something like a cure takes place through life itself, through pleasure, through the kindness he receives on every side — which he doesn't really want to accept because he is still a hypochondriac. And the anxiety demons torment him, if not with one trouble, then with another. So he is always swinging back and forth between Raimund the humorist and Raimund the hypochondriac. But at least he has given up the idea that he might go mad. That fear had obsessed him for years. Even so, he is still bound to animals. After ten years he gets another dog, and now see what happens: he plays with the dog and the dog really bites him. Again the thought of it overpowers him. He is standing there, he is bitten by the dog, and the dog has rabies! (Actually, it was established later that the dog did have rabies, but it was a very light case.) Now Raimund travels to Pottenstein, shoots himself in the head; the bullet lodges in the posterior cavity, far back. It can't be operated on. Raimund dies from the shot after three days.

You see how Raimund had freed himself from the first obsession, but karma continued to work. This is an example of karma working itself out completely, in a remarkable way. For only think! Subjectively, it is not precisely a suicide, for Raimund could not be called a fully responsible individual. Objectively, it is also not precisely a suicide, for if they had been able in those days to operate on that part of the head, Raimund would have been saved. At that time the operation was not possible and they had to leave the bullet in the head, so that after three days death was inevitable. So it is not a pure suicide, either subjectively or objectively. Thus one cannot say there will be consequences in the karma because of suicide. The karma does not continue: it was balanced out by what Raimund experienced in this incarnation up to his death, up to the way his suicidal intention was carried out. One sees clearly how karma from his earlier incarnation rises up and strikes him in this incarnation. One sees it reach across the span of time to strike with strength.

So now, first, we have seen that there are individuals whose ego, astral body, and etheric body develop, either suddenly or by stages, in such a way that they break into the spiritual world with a visionary capacity: St. Teresa, Mechthild of Magdeburg, and many others. There are such individuals who show an abnormality in one direction, the direction of spiritual awareness. They have been given some karmic gift — which we are only considering from the aspect of this particular earth-life. With these individuals we do not need to enter into karmic details. Naturally it is a fulfillment of karma. But one can understand the case from a single earth-life.

Then there are the individuals turned in the other direction. They develop abnormally in their physical-etheric organism; they sink down into their physical body and become pathological cases, as I showed you, in three stages. Their pathological condition is induced by their karma. But one only needs to look at the general picture. With such personalities as St. Teresa the individual became especially strong in earlier earth-lives, while in the pathological cases the individual became especially weak, causing the higher being to be drawn down into the lower organism. Again one needs only to look at a few general characteristics of an individual, one need not examine the karma in detail.

But now in Ferdinand Raimund we have an unusual

personality. He developed not only in the visionary direction but in the opposite direction also, and at the same time. We have the two opposites constantly pitted against each other throughout his life. Both the genius and the psychopath are in his personality; they play into each other, wonderfully and tragically. Thus this case obliges us to study the concrete details of his karma. We have to perceive how his karma works to create the two extremes, how it holds them apart, sometimes letting them work into each other. You will find countless places in Raimund's dramas where you can say his spiritual vision is active and at the same time something is working in from the anxiety demons. Sometimes you see it in the structure of the drama itself.

If we study human character in this way, we come inevitably to a consideration of karma. And we must see on the one hand the one-sidedness of that abstract teaching from certain ancient streams of civilization — namely, that illness comes from sin — which means that only abnormal spirituality is active in the human being. Naturally certain ideas can be expressed in this abstract way, but they remain theories even if one treats people in accordance with them. The opposite assertion is just as abstract and just as one-sided: that sin comes from illness, and that there are physical substances and processes in some people to be combated. First of all we have to investigate the concrete details of the total human organism, how its upper members relate to each other, whether they are separated from each other, whether they distance themselves from the lower members. Likewise, we must be able to see how karma is working in such an interplay of genius and pathology as was the case with Raimund. Those who achieve an understanding of these things will find opportunities in life to add something more to what they are already accomplishing in the work of physical healing, to add words that will make the healing process complete. They will reach the moment when they are no longer bound merely to a physical healing process, seeking the why and the wherefore of physical healing alone, for they will perceive how necessary it is in many cases to add a moral dimension to it. This does not mean one becomes sentimental and goes calling on a patient with all kinds of trifling consolations. Usually such things have little effect. Sick people haven't much energy left for weepy callers — or for hearty jollities either! They do have an amazing amount of energy left for what lies in natural human relations, not the "what" of words but the "how." One finds a way instinctively in such situations if one is able to express a view of the world and of life in a way that relates them to spiritual connections — as it can if one takes seriously such examples as I have described.

Spiritual activity cannot consist of talk, much less of religious tirades. Spiritual work must relate to facts. If it takes hold of facts, then it will be useful first of all to make the necessary connections with human beings. Then it can be used for healthy people and sick people. One will develop an instinct for orienting oneself to any illness with this or with that symptom. You will see that this extends to physical illnesses as well. But we must first open up the way to see that these things apply to physical illnesses. You will come to this if you study various examples of them, also the biographies of many geniuses. But not from the standpoint of that arch-philistine Lombroso! What is so disturbing about Lombroso's theory — his own great genius has to be acknowledged — is the fact that he is a thorough philistine, that on every page you read commonplace opinions. Science has fallen to that level! If one refuses to accept assertions from that kind of standpoint, if one directs one's activity from a really thoughtful perception of the world — that is, of physical and spiritual life — then if one needs to offer comfort to a sick person, one will offer the comfort of religion with a true spiri-tual aura. But not without clear understanding behind it. Whether one gives communion to sick people in the right way, so that they begin to improve, so that during their convalescence their soul is in no way injured, depends upon one's having an understanding for these things.

For certain convalescents, their physical healing will not be complete without the sacrament of communion, so that what had been brought into disarray in their karma can be put in order again. If one does not know that, one cannot carry it into the aura of the sacrament. But if physicians also understand these things, if they recognize karma working through the illness while keeping professional command of the healing process, they will be able to relate themselves to it in the right way. They must observe these things with their whole being from a broad worldview. Then something objective will happen for them, if they work consciously with their whole soul to help the karmic processes developing in the patient. Their healing mission will be the other half of divine service; it will have a religious dimension. They will learn to regard themselves as partners of the priests, standing beside the priests and administering the other half of the divine service. Healing then becomes a divine service. Things that the materialistic world conception has turned into nature worship — to dancing around the golden calf — these things must be returned and transformed to a divine service, through proper anthroposophical understanding. To transform everything in life and art and religion into the service of God: that will be the ultimate task of a comprehensive pastoral medicine that can be practiced within the anthroposophical movement. But a beginning must be made. It must be initiated here; at least the indications must be given for it to those who will carry the impulse forward, out of spiritual foundations, for the two sides of a true divine service.

That is why pastoral medicine is first being presented to priests and physicians within the anthroposophical movement. Those individuals will then find possibilities, with their knowledge of nature and spirit, to pursue pastoral medicine further. But they will also be able to use it to penetrate the specific regions of life that lie within their mission.

Lecture 7

IF ONE HAD NO OTHER MEANS OF INVESTIGATION than that
provided by modern science, one would never attain an understanding of the human being. Certainly it is not my wish to
belittle the accomplishments of this science in its own areas, for
as far as its methods allow it to go, it brilliantly explores whatever can have the slightest relevance to it. But one cannot reach
the human being by this means, because in human life in its
present form, physical-etheric body and soul-and-spirit are
interwoven. Present earth processes reach into the physical-
etheric body from every direction. With modern science we follow these physical-chemical processes of outer nature, that is, of
nature outside the human being. Comparatively speaking, this
science is good for the world outside us. People have simply
accepted the idea that just as these chemical processes occur in
a physics or chemistry laboratory, or in some piece of the world
that we are able to observe as our immediate environment, so
approximately they are also then continued within the human
being. For instance, combustion is described as the combining
of some substance or other with oxygen; then the thoughts
about this are continued unchanged when speaking of the
process within the human body, and combustion is still
described as happening the same way within us. But one should
know that this is not possible. For the process in a human being
that is analogous to combustion is related to external combustion precisely as something living is related to something dead.
Combustion in the external world is inorganic, lifeless, while
within a human being we have a combustion that has become
living. This fact is important for all of science. External combustion, so far as the substance it affects is concerned, is definitely subject to conditions of warmth. According to science,
there is a definite so-called flash point, and the heat of com-

bustion always relates to this external condition. This does not continue in the same way within the human organism. Externally, given a certain temperature, any substance can combine with oxygen and produce combustion. Within the human being the same temperature is not needed for that to happen; other laws prevail. This is important for external science, because external science sets up hypotheses that appear to be perfectly plausible. Earlier conditions are assumed from the conditions that now exist on the earth. Preyer, the famous Jena physiologist,[8] has done just that. He found the ordinary Kant-Laplace theory too stupid, so he went back to certain dynamic fire processes from which evolution was supposed to have originated. He also took it for granted that these must have happened at temperatures that today are necessary for similar fire processes to happen. That was not necessarily so. One can of course go in thought from the inorganic fire processes of this present age to similar processes in this age in the human organism, although actually these latter happen at an essentially lower temperature. But on this basis, even for a hypothetical view of original earth conditions, one would get quite different results. In short, with the means that modern science provides it is not possible to gain an understanding of the external world, either in its evolution or in its present state.

Naturally this causes difficulties if a certain attitude prevails. I can speak of these because I myself have experienced them with particular intensity. Through my whole life there has been one foremost characteristic — you will find it mentioned in my autobiography.[9] I can only describe it as the greatest possible respect for modern natural science. My respect has never changed. Never at any time would I have criticized in a trivial sense — which would be so easy to do — what natural science was bringing forward, whether in the field of external chemical, of mechanical or physical research, or of medicine. And yet at the same time evolution stood there before my eyes as a spiritual vision. And the need arose to bring what was opening up for me spiritually — for instance, the Atlantean time, or the

Lemurian time, or something still further back, or further forward — to bring that into harmony with what natural science was giving out. This has not been too difficult with what natural science says about the immediate present. But when it begins to exceed its bounds, to "go wild," when it advances hypotheses that reach from the present age to a time lying far in the past, we encounter the most severe conflicts if we want to bring what we have seen spiritually into harmony with what science is saying. We come into conflict with science just when we would like to be in accord with it. Spiritual science would never choose to be in disagreement with natural science. For surely one would not be so unintelligent as to oppose facts! All the more, then, one comes into conflict with opinions. As long as natural researchers talk, that is good. As soon as they begin writing, they really "go wild," and then one can no longer go along with what they say. This is a serious situation, and it must be reckoned with by anyone who has to relate in any way to what modern science is able to give.

Natural science simply does not reach as far as the human being. Human beings have a soul nature and a spiritual nature, and do not have just a physical organism with physical processes that can be investigated externally — even to such phenomena as those of aerodynamics or thermodynamics. We also have living in us our karma from earlier earth-lives; we see it manifesting in our personality. We found this plainly evident in such a person as Ferdinand Raimund. But there is no possibility of exploring such connections if we only have the means of modern science at our disposal.

We must indeed advance to a new level. We must begin from the side of spiritual science to look at what manifests as external human processes and relate them to what we see as spiritual processes. We will be going in the right direction, for instance, if, holding fast to the physiology of breathing and circulation as we already know it from current natural science, we proceed further to examine how physical life is connected with spiritual life.

Let us look at human inhalation. It consists of our taking in external gaseous substance. But this is not just a passive happening, something being taken in by a human being in a completed condition and elaborated within. It is not just changing over from one process, inhalation, to another process, exhalation — from the inhaling of oxygen to the forming of carbon dioxide. The inhalation process shows itself in reality to be continuously creating the human being, working continuously to build the human being, from without inwards. In the inhalation process we find there is a constant building up, proceeding inward from the cosmos. Human beings do not merely inhale amorphous oxygen. In the oxygen that we regard, mistakenly, simply as a gaseous substance we inhale formative forces appropriate to our own being. If sometimes we have shortness of breath, some alien elemental is lying across the path of our breathing. That occurs in abnormal breathing. But in normal breathing, there is always a human being coming into being. Continuously a human birth is occurring out of the macrocosm; an air-human is being born into the human. The entire process is an activity of the astral body. We must picture it in this way: We inhale. The inhaling is activated by the astral body. The entire process is a continuous being-born. It takes place in the element of air, in everything that is air within us. We have a perpetual human birth in the element of air in the inhalation process.

But now we also breathe out. We breathe out carbon dioxide. At the conclusion of other organic processes carbon dioxide is, in a certain sense, collected for outbreathing. That too is commonly presented as a kind of passive reaction, or something similar. People simply do the research they are able to do in this field with physical means, and they don't arrive at a clear conception. Now the exhalation also is activated. It is not just some passive human process. There is activity in it: activity of the etheric body. The entire process occurs in the fluid element, the element that in earlier times was called water, when everything that was fluid was called water. We can continue to use the expression. This process takes place in the element of water.

Now there should come an important question: how is it during sleep? In sleep the etheric body is first and foremost within the human organism; therefore for exhalation there is no problem. But how can we inhale during sleep if the astral body is outside? Well, the fact is that during sleep actually only the microcosmic part of the astral body goes out of the physical organism; the macrocosmic astrality is all the more active at that time. All the astrality of the macrocosm enters during sleep. Our breathing activity during sleep is for this reason very different from our breathing activity while awake, because it is regulated by the activity of the macrocosm. So there is an essential difference between inhalation while awake and inhalation while asleep. The control of our inhalation during sleep comes from outside. When we are awake we control our inhalation ourselves through our astral body, from within outwards. While we are asleep the cosmic astrality enters our organism to do this for us. Here you have an important clue by which to approach questions of pathology. The cosmos has this remarkable attribute. You find that it holds a healthy relation to earth conditions if you go far enough above the earth. Close to the earth there are all kinds of influences through climate and other circumstances that can make the cosmic astrality abnormal. Similarly, through other processes that we have yet to learn about, the inner astrality of the human being can become abnormal. There we have the source of a certain kind of pathological condition, but the source is within, in soul and spirit. That is an essential fact.

Now let us go further. The breathing process is comparatively coarse. We breathe gaseous substance in and we breathe gaseous substance out. The whole process is coarse as compared to all the other processes that occur in us as well as in the macrocosm — for instance, those that have to do with the fluctuation of heat, with the element of warmth inside and outside the human being. There are differentiations of warmth inside the human being and differentiations outside the human being. We can think away air, water, earth, and hold before us only these differences in warmth. To physicists this makes no sense, because they regard warmth only as a condition of a material substance. But spiritual science knows that in warmth one has to do with a separate element. We can speak of warmth as an independent active element. Now fundamental to our entire human life there is a receptive process that is finer than the breathing process. It is the warmth process. When we examine the human lung region, when we study the organization of the lungs, we are looking at the coarse breathing process in the element of air. But when we come up higher to the region centered primarily in the head (although it is present to a smaller degree in the entire human organism), we come to a finer breathing process that occurs not in the element of air but in the element of warmth. Therefore we can say: higher up, we come to a finer process consisting of an extraordinarily fine reception of warmth from the macrocosm, breathing-in of warmth and breathing-out of warmth. But now this is what we must see: in the coarse inhalation-exhalation of the lungs, the human being is participating in an active exchange with the outer world: breathing in, breathing out, breathing in, breathing out, in, out, in, out. The process I am now describing is not like that. There is indeed an "in," but there is not an "out" in the same sense as in ordinary breathing. In this warmth-breathing the exhalation actually takes place within the human being; it is an inner process. What is exhaled by the nerve-sense system becomes united with what is being inhaled by the lungs. Thus the nerve-sense system carries on a very fine breathing process of which the inhalation is indeed a taking-in from outside, but what is taken in is not released again to the outside. It is given over to the coarser breathing process of the lungs, to the air inhalation, and is then by way of that air inhalation carried farther into the organism.

We can perceive the following process: The cosmic warmth enters the human organism by way of breathing. But not only warmth. The warmth carries with it light, macrocosmic chemism, and macrocosmic life, vitality. Light ether, chemical ether, and life ether from the macrocosm are carried by the inhalation of warmth into the human organism. The element of warmth carries light, as well as the chemical and life elements, into the human being, and gives them over to the air-inhalation process. This entire process, which lies over the air-breathing process and which appears as a refined (or even metamorphosed) breathing process, is not studied today in a real sense. It is lacking entirely from physiology — well, a bit of it falls into physiology and works there as a foreign body. This is an example of how one gets nowhere if one works separately from the spirit on one side and from nature on the other. It is something entirely foreign to the physiology of the senses as the latter is commonly presented, with the various senses — seeing, hearing, sensation of warmth — totally differentiated. In reality, they are only the limbs, the outer shoots of this other process that, to begin with, is the taking-in of warmth and with it light, chemism, and life. This is different from the sense process. As it is now, people know only the peripheral aspects of the sense process, not this central activity; that's why the current physiology of the senses is like a completely foreign body to them. Physiologists dabble around in the separate senses and treat them in a dilettantish fashion. And they pile hypothesis upon hypothesis. Of course this is bound to happen because they are looking at the single, separate processes of seeing, hearing, and so forth, and are completely missing the fact that all the senses flow in together, stream in together into the human being. No one sees that all this flows in, is taken in together with the taking in of warmth and the light, chemism, and life that warmth carries in with it from the macrocosm. Only after that does one come to the breathing of the lungs.

There will only be a real physiology of the senses when the physiologist is able to say: I follow the physical, physiological processes of the eye to the nerve, which then carries the process inward; I come gradually to the path of the breathing, out of the paths of the senses and thinking to the breathing. Then it will be understood how yoga could come about in earth-life: that is, by disregarding the sense life that takes its course at the periphery. In the practice of yoga, activity goes entirely into a conscious inhalation process; what lies behind it, namely, sense perception, is made the object of consciousness through the breathing activity. You see, in earlier world conceptions, such things were known and put into practice instinctively. But modern science will surely encounter riddles everywhere, because it is not able to see facts and make the connection between them. It observes eye and ear; then it begins to speculate wildly about what happens inside. And if it notices that the hypothesis it attempts as it follows eye and ear inward leads to a blind alley — because it will not accept as fact the finer breathing process that I have presented — then it says, "Why, of course, what goes on inside is simply paralleling what goes on outside." Parallelism — the processes occur at the same time! Well, that's a very convenient way out!

This should provide firm ground for both priest and physician in connection with contemporary knowledge, for they will no longer have to reject this knowledge. The physiology of the senses has gathered tremendous treasures from all sides, but it is like a man who has collected the most excellent building materials for a beautiful house and carries them to a place and arrange them in an enormous pile, but then he can't build the house. He can't possibly build the house. Everything that occurs in the senses has been gathered together and arranged in a great pile, but no work starts. To start the work, what goes on inside the human being has to be added to what has already been researched externally. Inquiry must be made into the process of the finer breathing that takes place in the etheric and astral bodies. From there one can go on to build the house. Naturally, when the house can be built one would be a fool to say: The first thing we have to do is to get rid of this great pile of building materials lying here. We will certainly not say that. Now that it is all there, we can begin to build the house.

It would be just as foolish to do what many people do today who look at things in a dilettantish way — that is, criticize natural science from the ground up and reject it. It does not have to be rejected. Every piece of the building material can be used, it is all valuable, and there will be a fine result if all that is given out today by the physiology of the senses is used. But as it is now, it is just a pile of material. So we can say: We extend our view from what takes place in ordinary breathing as the continuous creation of present-day human beings to the finer breathing process that takes place higher up in the element of warmth, into which the entire cosmic etheric world plays. That is what we see if we study the upper human being.

But we can also look below in the air-breathing and study the lower human being. Then, just as we reach in air inhalation a higher, finer process, so now in air exhalation we reach a lower, coarser process. Below we gradually go from the inner activity of forming carbon dioxide to the process of digestion. Above, we had to connect air inhalation with that finer nerve-sense process that becomes a spiritual activity. Below we have to connect air exhalation with the digestive process, where the human activity gradually becomes purely physical, becomes altogether a metabolic activity of the physical body — which is a modified exhalation. In a certain sense, the activity that exhalation leaves behind within us is the metabolism. Just as what breathing takes in of nerve-sense spirit activity becomes inner activity, so what remains behind of inner activity from exhalation becomes the sum of forces forming metabolism. The metabolism is active in the element that in earlier epochs was called earth, the name for everything in the human organism that tends toward solidity.

If we now study the entire process more closely, we find it has four parts. We have the process that we have just characterized, of which we can say that exhalation really goes into the human being. If we look at our ordinary external inhalation, we see a union of what is inhaled with what comes down from above. With exhalation, we have to say the opposite. Exhalation leaves forces behind for metabolism. It does not take something up; it gives something away. So we have an inner inhalation as well as an inner exhalation. The union of this inner inhalation with what the physical body does is the actual metabolic digestive process.

And now if you look carefully at this fourfold differentiation, you will see the human being in a new light, for the following facts also appear. Here is the path of the warmth element coming into the human being and bringing light, chemism, and life. It connects itself with the breathing and gives chemism and life to it. But it does not give light to the breathing. It holds that back. The light stays behind and floods the human being as inner light, becoming thought activity.

Also, as inhalation and exhalation proceed, the macrocosmic chemism is given off and becomes inner chemism — which is something different from the chemistry with which we are acquainted in our ordinary laboratory work. Macrocosmic chemism is introduced into the human being by this extension of the inner breathing process. So we can say that here chemism is introduced. Also the life ether goes in and is taken up by the human being through the interplay of exhalation and metabolism.

So if we follow the process from above to below, we have light coming in by way of the warmth ether, and then coming to a stop. Where the breathing enters, it comes to a "stop!" for the light. The light spreads itself out. It is not carried farther by the human organism; it can spread out as light. We carry within us a pure light organism, a light organism that thinks.

We follow the process farther inward to where inhalation borders on exhalation, and we find the chemism is carried in to that point through the nerve-sense process. Now the chemism comes to a stop. It is an inner chemism, a chemical organism in us that feels.

Now let us go down further to where exhalation leaves the digestive-metabolic process behind — not the external metabolic process of food consumption, but the inner metabolic activity. There it is "stop!" for the life ether. The life ether forms a human organism that wills. Thus thinking, feeling, and willing come about.

We can now follow the entire process as it is reflected in our physical body. Take everything that is above: within, it manifests as thinking, but thinking is unsubstantial. Behind it lies all I have described to you that happens along the nerve paths. They are the external, physical paths for thinking.

Now go to the next process. You have this, the uppermost process in the human being, taken in through the breathing; it manifests in physical reflection as the arterial circulation. The arterial circulation is the second kind of path.

Then we come to the third process, which takes place between exhalation and metabolism. This also has its own path, the veins. So the third path is the venous circulation.

Now if we go still farther into the human being we find the process that provides a path for itself from below, from outside. It is the process by which the life ether is taken up. It must provide the life ether for itself from outside, from below. We find the physical projection of this in the lymph formation and the lymph system.

So now you have the relation between outer and inner. Very much lies behind the nerve-sense inhalation. It is an incoming activity, and in what lies behind it there is much that remains unknown to us. Karma is active there, karma from the previous earth-life. It is not perceptible, but it streams in. Karma streams in. If with spiritual vision one investigates the nerve paths, if one investigates how they are formed in relation to the senses, one finds on these paths: karma. Karma streams in. On the other hand, in the lymph formation one does not only find a physical process: the fact that lymph enters the organism by the lymph vessels lets one see how lymph goes into the blood and takes care of us in that way Johannes Müller, the well-known physiologist,[10] has already said, "What is lymph? Lymph is blood without any red corpuscles. And blood? Blood is lymph with red corpuscles." This is, of course, a broad statement, but it is correct in a certain way. We see in lymph everything that has not yet become blood; we see in it also the living-weaving of developing karma. In the lymph process new karma is forming. The lymph vessels are the beginning of the paths of future karma.

So as you approach the human being from the world of spirit and perceive that macrocosmic light, chemism, and life are brought on paths of warmth, as you come from the light to the life paths and see the general cosmic life flowing in, you perceive more and more the flowing-in of karma which then becomes active in the human being's earth-life between birth and death. It works its way in through the nerves; it moves forward through the modified arterial process, and then is held back, dammed up in the venous process. When it reaches the venous process it pushes itself in on mysterious waves. And as we form venous blood we get this piling-up of karma within us, and then we act from karmic impulses.

A change in the blood can merely mean anger. On the other hand, what piles up there because the past is not allowed down into the venous process leads to actions that bring about the shaping of karma.

What the lymph does not allow to go over into the blood gathers deep in the subconscious. It forms a seed in the subconscious, a seed that we carry out with us through the gate of death when we throw off our physical body. It is the karma-to-be, the karma still to be developed.

Above, in the breathing process one perceives the karma that comes out of the past. Below the exhalation, in the circulation where the lymph has not yet become blood, one sees the latent karma. It stays in the lymph. So one can say that karma flows into the human arterial process and stays behind; the venous process is formed and karma comes into being again. We have here the borderline where karma begins to pile up in the nerve-sense-arterial process.

Below, corresponding to the process that goes from lymph to veins, we have incoming karma. When we look with spiritual eyes at the lymph that has not yet become blood, we see outgoing karma. Thus we have the connection between physical and spiritual. Above, the human being qualitatively comes close to the spiritual and touches karma. In between, the present life is dammed up. Below, in the lymph not yet become blood, we see the new karma arising, beginning to be formed. Between past karma and karma that is forming, in between stands the human earth-life, which — looked at from this point of view — is a damming-up between the two. Thus we can follow the procedure right into the physical process.

You can realize that we are coming more and more to see the spiritual working in the physical. Only this will perfect our practical work.

LECTURE 8

WE HAVE EXAMINED THE HUMAN CONSTITUTION as far as it can be seen in human beings themselves or in connection with their immediate environment. Now we must go out beyond humanity. For everywhere humanity stands in some relation to the forces in the universe, and one can only understand these various relations if one explores the immense diversity of the universe itself.

Just think how manifold the forces in the universe are! Look at a growing plant, for instance. Follow the growth of its stem upward from the earth's surface, and the growth of its root downward. Right there are two opposite tendencies within the plant: a striving upward and a striving downward. And if today we were far enough along in scientific research — so often used for less important matters — to use it for such a thing as the growth of a stem upward and the growth of a root downward, we would find the connections in the universe that would then finally explain the totality: humanity and the world, microcosm and macrocosm. For we would find that everything connected with the stem's upward growth has some relation to the unfolding of the sun's forces in the course of the day, in the course of the year, even beyond the year. And we would find that everything connected with the root's downward growth has some relation to the moon's forces and the moon's changes. If therefore we look at a plant properly, we already come to see through its form a relation between sun and moon. We have, so to speak, to extract the simple image of a plant from the whole universe, from all the forces in the universe.

Someone who is really observant will never see the root other than striving downward into the earth and at the same time rounding itself. The root rounding itself into the earth — that is the picture of the root that one must have, the rounding

form pushing into the ground. We must see the stem differently as it unfolds in an upward direction. Someone who combines
sensitivity with observation will have the definite feeling that
the stem strives to stream out as a line. The root wants to unfold
in a rounding, circular direction; the stem wants to unfold in a
linear direction. That is the archetypal form of the plant. And in
the linear striving upward we must see the presence of sun forces
on the earth. In the root's striving toward roundness we must see
the presence of moon forces on the earth.

Now let us look further. We think of the sun as being at a
great height and of the plant as streaming to reach it. But the
plant does more than just reach upward; it reaches out in width,
it creates peripheries. And we find within its upward striving
that something else is active, at first just at its top in the blossoms we find the forces of Venus working with the sun forces.
Then as blossoms unfold below, as leaves come, moving inward
from the periphery, we find the forces of Mercury working. On
the one hand if we want to understand the structure of the plant
as it pushes toward the Sun, we must see that the sun forces are
helped by the forces of Venus and Mercury.

On the other hand we must realize that these forces alone
would not be able to form the plant. With them alone, the
plant-being would in a certain sense only attain a compact,
solid form. For it to unfold as one sees it, for instance, in the
most extreme example in a tree, there are forces working everywhere counter to the Venus and Mercury forces: namely, the
forces of Mars, Jupiter, and Saturn. Thus in addition to the basic
polarity of sun activity and moon activity, there is also the activity of all the other planets in the universe.

In the plant you have the entire planetary system in front of
you. It is right there on the earth. And perhaps it is not so
ridiculous that a scholar — a half or three-quarters scholar as
Paracelsus[11] was — made such a statement as this: "When you
eat a plant you're eating the entire planetary system. For all those
forces are contained in it." Paracelsus said it like this: "With the
plant you eat the whole heaven." The world is indeed formed in

such manifold variety that one does have in one's immediate environment the forces of the entire macrocosm — in growth, in structure, in the disposition of all living things.

Now let us get back to the human being. We showed yesterday that one can go from the area of lung breathing to a higher area where there is a finer inhalation. And we discovered that this finer inhalation carries karmic streams in from the past. We can go still further. If we have working into the human being what I would like for the moment to call a refined breath stream, we can say the following: If one would unfold only what lies in the astral body and ego, one would never reach the sun, with the human constitution as it is at the present time. When one is in the ego and astral body during sleep, one does not reach the sun sphere. There is only darkness. If one were to live in the astral body and ego without any connection to the etheric and physical bodies, one would not come to the sun. How, then, does this happen?

Let us consider first what the situation is when the astral body and ego approach the etheric body. In clairvoyance one can bring this condition about fairly easily, by strengthening thinking — strengthening it by very thorough, energetic meditation. Then it is easy to come to this condition; it is the beginning of initiation. One slips down into the etheric body but is not yet able to take hold of the physical body; one remains in the etheric body. In this condition it is possible to think very, very well. One sees nothing, hears nothing, but one can think very well. Thinking is not in the least extinguished, but seeing, hearing, and the other sense activities are suppressed. At first, thinking remains the same, except that one can think more than previously. One can think such thoughts as we are expressing here, for instance thoughts about the macrocosm. Thinking becomes wider. One knows clearly: "now I am in the etheric world." Thus when one is in the etheric body, one is truly in the world ether. One has the clear experience of this: "I am in the spiritual world out of which the sense world comes." But one is not able to differentiate between spiritual world and sense world, one is beyond a differentiated sense world. The sun no longer shines, the stars no longer shine, there is no moonlight. There is no longer a clear distinction between the kingdoms of nature on the earth. A person only has that faculty when down in the physical body in normal life or in a higher stage of initiation. But in exchange for the blurring of the contours of the sense world, there is a general spirituality, the weaving life of the spirit.

If one goes further, if one takes conscious hold of the physical body and begins to live in the organs, the perceptions that had become dim or had vanished begin to emerge again (with the exception of earthly forms) as spirit entities. Where earlier in ordinary consciousness one had seen the sun and then it had become dark, foggy, but had still been within the general weaving spirituality, now there appear beings of the second hierarchy. Now one can differentiate in the spiritual world. Moon and stars appear again, but in their spiritual aspect: they are now spiritual colonies — they can be called that, or something similar. Now one understands how in ordinary everyday consciousness humankind sees the sun, for instance, in its physical form, and the same with other things, but when someone has entered consciously into a physical body, and has actually taken hold of it in its spiritual dimension; the sun is seen as a spiritual being, and the same with the whole world. Now we know that with each sun ray shining down upon us during the day, spirit is also entering us. Through every sense experience spirit is entering us. We have therefore to regard the higher, finer breathing as a breathing that is continuously impregnated by spirit. And we perceive that the sun is living in every sense perception that streams into us. It is indeed the spirit of the sun, or the spirits of the sun. The sun is present in every sense perception. In our finer breathing the sun force, the sun life is streaming straight into us.

So you see the relation humanity has to the sun. When a ray of light streams into your eye, the sun spirit is streaming in with that ray of light. The spirit of the sun is the substance of the finer breathing. With our sense perceptions we breathe in the manifold ingredients of the spiritual sun. You have there an important view of the human being from one direction. As one unfolds in an etheric body, one develops in the etheric body thinking — the thoughts of the universe. These thoughts of the universe in which one finds oneself when living consciously in an etheric body are at first devoid of warmth or cold, devoid of tone. They are a kind of vague feeling in which one's feeling of self merges with one's feeling of the macrocosm. But if now one takes hold of the physical body, one enters into the spirit of the sense perceptions. And the thoughts are infused from various sides: through the eyes, the sun essence — thought — that is breathed in is infused with color; through the ear, thought is tinted with tone; through the organ of warmth, thought is tinted with warmth or cold. There you have the cosmic relation of thought to sense perception. Thought must be understood as preceding the sense experience; then the sense experience comes through infusion, tinted by the sun.

Humankind simply does not realize that the sun-being streams into us with every sense perception. And on the path of the sun, past karma streams in too. It is by no means a childish image to think of the sun as a receptacle of past karma. If we understand the human head properly, we must say the spiritual sun rays stream in invisibly and are transformed as they stream in into something physical, which then appears as merely a physical attribute in the world of color; tone, warmth. And at the same time, on the path of these sun rays that slip in through the senses into the nerves, karma enters into us. That is one side of the human being.

Now let us look at the other side. Karma goes out at that place in the organism where the lymph is, the place where everything is alive and active that has not yet been drawn into the blood. There we find outgoing karma. What are the paths of outgoing karma? To know that, we must acquaint ourselves through spiritual science with the moon forces.

And now if we gradually come from the etheric world to which we have become accustomed and take hold of the physical body in its periphery, the area of the senses, then all the life streaming in from the sun and bringing our past karma with it appears to be bringing reproach, and to be doing much to disturb us. But far more important than the disturbing elements in our karma is this knowledge, this insight that we can attain. It is by virtue of our past that we have become what we now are. The life of our inner being is enriched by the perception of the sun entering on the paths of the senses and nerves. If we can separate ourselves from our karma and concentrate on the instreaming forces of the spiritual sun, we will experience an infinite happiness as we receive them. We will wish that the sun element were in us perpetually; we cannot help longing for it. The sun element enters into us lovingly if we wish it; it is what we know in physical life in a weaker form as our active human love. This is the interplay of sun activity with the human inner world, the loving penetration of the sun into humans and into everything that wants to sprout and grow and thrive in humans. The living sun rays enter lovingly. Here love is not merely a soul-spiritual force: it is the force that calls everything physical to germinate and sprout and grow, everything that can be beneficial to humans in every way when they value it. This is the force of which a human being is aware through direct outer vision.

Now if one takes hold of the physical body in the other direction, in the direction of the forces that develop the lymph and prepare it for entering into the blood, one becomes aware of the activity of the moon. This is of quite a different character. On the one hand we can say the spiritual sun is active in the way we have indicated; on the other hand the moon is active. When we work to grasp the process of the lymph-blood formation inwardly, we find we are entering into the activity of the moon. And we have the constant feeling that the moon wants to take something away from us, to lift something out of us. With the sun we had the feeling that it wants continually to give us something. With the moon we have the feeling that it wants continually to take something out of us. And if we are not alert while we are observing the moon's activity, when we have consciously taken hold of the physical body and are engrossed in the lymph-blood formation, if we are not absolutely alert and in complete control of our vision, suddenly the continuity is broken and standing there before us is a spiritual being similar to ourselves but distorted, almost a caricature of ourselves, a being we have brought to birth. We would miss this emanation if we were not alert. But it does not seem particularly strange to us as it separates from us and confronts us. It is hardly more than an enhanced view of ourselves in a mirror. When we look at ourselves in an ordinary mirror, that is the physical world. When we see ourselves reflected in the etheric world by the moon forces, that is a higher kind of mirroring.

Let us review the whole process. There is nothing particularly amazing about it. But it shows us that we are indeed connected with the universe. That the moon is continually separating forces from us, which then it makes independent, forces that were living in us and that then go out into the spiritual world, streaming out into the macrocosm, constantly carrying images out of us into the macrocosm. But now think how it could be if such an image, which the moon forces are continually producing in humanity and which then they want to take out of us to carry into the distances of the world, if such an image were held back in the human body and kept there. And not merely an image, an abstraction, but a form permeated by forces.

How could such a form be retained in the human being? We have the moon forces continually striving to pull and draw the human image out. How could this form be held back? It can remain in humans if the sun forces are brought in deeply enough from another side. Then the form remains in the human being; then an embryonic life begins. Fructification consists of nothing else than that the sun forces are drawn down to where the moon forces are active in the lymph. Thereby the image that would otherwise go out takes hold of physical matter in the human body. What otherwise is a mere image now takes on physical form. For this to happen, sun forces combine with moon forces in the lymph system of the human organism.

Let us look at the other side. We can also investigate the moon forces higher up: then we find that the opposite happens. Then the human being is not formed again in the human body, but the sun macrocosm is given form in the human. Now we have a different view of the macrocosm. When the embryo is formed, a physical world arises within the human being that must come out. When on the other hand the moon forces activate their desire nature — they want to capture and draw down the sun forces — then the spirit in the universe comes into being within the human. The spirit of the universe is engendered, a spiritual embryo. Then the possibility is given for forming what must come in from the spiritual world, what has been in the spiritual world up to the time of a new earth-life and now comes in as spirit embryo. Then, the union of the two takes place in the human being.

If we explore these things, we come to see that they are completely interwoven. Then we have the true explanation of the human being's relation to the universe.

Now help comes from every direction. The sun activity that is uniting here with the moon activity has the help of Mars, Jupiter, and Saturn. What, then, are the tasks of Mars, Jupiter, and Saturn? Recall, dear friends, what I said yesterday. When the sun forces are going in, first they must stop for the light; second, they must stop for the macrocosmic chemism; third, they must stop for the life. The Saturn forces bring about the stop for the light, the Jupiter forces in their wisdom bring about the stop for the world chemism, the Mars forces the stop for the life. There you have in detail the drawing-in of the sun forces modified by the forces of the so-called outer planets.

From the opposite direction you have the moon forces modified. When they work alone in their full strength, they bring about the formation of the embryo, that is, the physical formation. When they are less strong, they do not enter into physical matter but stay in the direction of the spirit, combining with the Venus forces of soul love. They can be still weaker — when they unite with what comes from the other side, the forces of Mercury, the divine messenger, who in ordinary everyday earth-life leads the lower forces up to the higher.

If we look out at the plant world spread as it is around us, we find the sun, moon, and stars everywhere. If we look within the human being, the sun, moon, and stars are there too, in exact correspondence. When something within is not in order, there is some trouble in the inner collaboration of sun, moon, and stars. If we as therapists want to restore it to order again, we must search in outer nature for a corresponding Saturn activity, for instance, that will work therapeutically on an unhealthy moon activity — and so forth. It is all out there. You see people will begin to have confidence in medicine again when they see that in the inner constitution the human being comprises the whole world. This is the knowledge we would like to bring to medicine again, knowledge it once had. The world will only have its trust in medicine restored when these things are once again understood.

But now let us look at the other side. Look first at the moon activity in human beings. See how it is striving continually to draw the human element out, to carry it into the universe. Let the picture stand before us — the human being striving to get out, wanting to be carried into the universe. This must not be presented to humanity as an abstraction, this shattering secret, but in picture form — the moon working continually to lift human beings out of themselves, to show them their relation to the macrocosm. The human being comes into earth-life as an embryo within another human being. But when this moon activity is enhanced by Venus and Mercury activity, then the human being is born not physically, but spiritually. If we add to the physical birth what we can invoke of Mercury and Venus activity, we bring about a spiritual birth. The human being is then born spiritually, outside, in the universe. We baptize the human being.

The working of the physical sun is always present in human beings. We can add to that perception a consciousness that the spiritual sun also is active in us, that on the paths of the physical-etheric sunlight, the light rays, chemical rays and life rays, the spirit is also pouring in. Spirit enters humans by way of the same paths that the physical-etheric sun activity enters: through the senses. In the same way that human beings perceive in everyday physical life the physical-etheric activity of the sun, we enable them to perceive the soul-spiritual activity of the sun. We give them communion.

Going out from the communion, we find on the one hand what is related to the help the sun is given: the darkening that relates to the light, the constant nearness of death to life. We go to the outer planets that are connected with the sun, and we add to the communion at the proper moment the anointing.

Or we go into human beings, and before they have any thought of the macrocosm, we hold them fast in their inner life, wanting not merely to give them their place as human beings in the macrocosm, but wanting to plant the macrocosm in them — in picture form, so that it becomes a seed developing in them. We give them confirmation.

If individuals receiving the sacraments live in them with full consciousness, they will be continually healed by them — healed of the universal illness to which they succumb, or are in constant danger of succumbing *in statu nascendi* simply by reason of their having incarnated in the physical material world. This is the priest's task.

It can also happen that an individual is by nature continually *in statu nascendi* of wanting to be free in the spiritual world, wanting to get out of the physical world, yet is obliged to remain in it during earth-life. And this causes in the organism not a state of unspirituality but a state of superspirituality, that is, illness. Medical measures must be prescribed, the opposite pole to the sacraments, when illness appears. This is the physician's task.

Thus we see on the one side the spiritual healing of the priest, and on the other side the priestly attitude of the physician, the physical healer. If we recognize how their tasks can be coordinated, we have grasped the significant connection between pastoral work and medical work. Then pastoral medicine is not just a theory, but embraces the working together of human beings.

LECTURE 9

SEPTEMBER 16, 1924

YOU HAVE SEEN HOW NECESSARY IT IS to relate a state of illness in a human being to his or her spiritual life and experience. The understanding that should be brought to illness by the two groups of people who have especially to do with pastoral medicine can really only come from such a point of view. Therefore I would like once more to consider the actual state of illness in connection with a person's spiritual life, this time from a standpoint that I think will throw greatest light upon the nature of illness.

As human beings we alternate between waking and sleeping. You all know in general what can be said from our perspective about these two conditions.

Let us hold clearly in our minds what really happens in the human being during sleep. The physical body and etheric body are by themselves; the astral body and ego are also by themselves. Turning first to the physical and etheric bodies, we know that by virtue of what these bodies are, certain processes go on that during the person's sleep are independent of the activity of the astral body and ego. In the human organism we find processes going on that are not at all suited to it in the way they must play themselves out. The physical body has to do with physical processes. Physical processes take their course outside in the mineral kingdom; they are suited to the mineral kingdom. They are not at all suited to the constitution of the human physical body. And yet while it is asleep this human body is, so to speak, subject to these physical processes in the same way that the mineral kingdom is. We must be aware of this contradiction in the human being precisely during sleep. During sleep the human being ought to be a world of physically active forces and substances, but this is something that really cannot be. That is why processes that go on in the physical body during sleep — unless they are brought into balance — cause illness.

The general assertion that sleep is healthful is correct in a certain sense, but only under certain conditions. And it must not prevent us from examining the true situation without prejudice. Physical processes in the human physical body can only be healthful when the ego and astral organization are down in the physical body, as is the normal condition during waking life. It is constantly interrupted by the sleep condition. Normally, however, even during sleep the catabolic process is still always going on in the physical body; it must be there so that the soul-life and spiritual life as a whole can really unfold. For the spiritual life is not connected with anabolic processes, only with catabolic processes. During sleep, therefore, there must be just as much of the catabolic processes as a person needs for waking life to unfold the next morning. If too many catabolic processes are there because of some unhealthy sleep condition, a residue of these processes piles up in the human organism, and then we have the inner cause for an illness.

If we extend our investigation to the etheric body, we find that during sleep only the processes can take place in the etheric body that can otherwise take place in the plant kingdom. During daytime consciousness, when the astral body and ego are in the etheric body, these processes are always raised to a higher level. But from the moment of a person's going to sleep to the moment of waking, they take their course in the same way that they do in the plant kingdom. Thus they too are not suited to the human organism; they need to be balanced by the astral body and ego. If they create a residue, this too is cause for illness. So we can say that sleep can show us how causes of illness really originate in the human organism. For they are fundamentally the normal sleep processes; at the same time they are the basis for human soul-spiritual life. And that points to a secret of this world — that whenever one penetrates to reality, one finds it has two sides! On one side, in the sleep condition of the human physical and etheric bodies we find the basis for spiritual development; on the other side, in the very same processes we find the basis for illnesses. Thereby illness is brought into direct connection with human spiritual development. Thus if we study what is active during sleep in the human physical and etheric bodies, we find the fundamental causes of illness.

Now let us consider from this point of view those who during waking life do not go down deeply enough into their physical and etheric bodies — which is what we have found to be the case in the mentally retarded or the psychopath. With such people the soul and spirit enter into processes of illness and live with them. Special value should be laid on this knowledge, that psychopaths and the so-called mentally disturbed are always closely involved in their inner lives with the causes of illness. You see, one has to look at such things carefully.

But now let us go to the outer world. Let us start from the human physical body and consider the outer mineral world that relates to it. During sleep we have processes in the human physical body from which the ego is missing. They go on without really any inner working "motor." But there is ego out there in the world in all those mineral processes. In them is what we can call world-ego. So we have on the one hand within the processes of the human physical body a condition of non-ego, a sum of processes that are egoless, processes that lack ego. And we have on the other hand in our outer environment a sum of mineral processes and mineral substances that are permeated by ego — that means, by all the hierarchies who are to be identified with ego. Mineral substance has ego.

Therefore let us assume that we observe in some person's physical body a process that should not be there, a sick process. It lacks ego. What can we do if we want to cure this condition? We can search outside in the mineral kingdom for that part of the ego that the person lacks, to cure what is too much asleep, to cure what is still continuing to sleep during waking life. Then we have the right remedy. If you give the substance that has an affinity to the sick organ, the ego-force that the organ lacked is brought into the organ. This is the principle underlying our search in inorganic nature around us for medicinal remedies for the physical body of the sick person. We have to find the corresponding substance that has ego-force; then it has a healing effect. Thus the transition from pathology to therapy rests upon a correct insight into the relation between the processes of the human physical body and the outer mineral world on the one hand, and the relation of the human etheric body to the plant world on the other. If we observe too exuberant a growth in the etheric body, we realize that the etheric body is lacking proper penetration by the astral body. Then we must search in the plant kingdom for the proper corresponding remedy. This is the direction our work must take.

One must recognize the spirit in nature, the spirit that is in the mineral and plant kingdoms of the world. It is the spirit, not the substance, that one must know, because in reality one heals the human being through the spirit that is in the mineral and in the plant. In its nature substance is not truly governed by spirit, but even so it has spirit in it. And those who want to heal without recognizing the spirit in stones and plants can only grope their way through traditional theory. They can try one thing or another and see whether it helps, but they will never know *why* it helps — because they will never know just where the spirit is in possession of some mineral or how it is in possession of it. To be a healer requires first and foremost a spiritual outlook on the world. And indeed this is the greatest anomaly of our time: that it is medicine itself that has the frightful disease of materialism. Medicine is seriously ill with materialism. It has become blind and is falling asleep, and this is creating harmful soul substances in science. It really needs to be healed. One can indeed say, the sickest entity of our time is not Turkey,[12] as was the case in nineteenth-century Europe, but the medical profession. This is a fact that physicians should know — as well as the theologians, for then perhaps the secret will remain among those to whom it has been entrusted!

Let us look at these things more closely. There are certain persons who are not psychopathic or insane in the sense in which one is justified in using those terms, but who nevertheless illustrate what I have been talking about during the last few days.

They descend into their physical and etheric bodies in such a way that they acquire a certain perceptible connection to their sick condition, to sick processes. These are sleepwalkers, whose peculiar state is not make-believe; it has often been described to the general public, and every initiate knows it well. While they are in their somnambulistic condition, they describe their illnesses. They go down into their physical and etheric body. Now the normal human being in waking life has the physical and etheric bodies completely saturated by the astral body and the ego. In the case of these sick individuals, the ego and astral body do not combine with the etheric and physical body in accordance (figuratively speaking) with their exact atomic weight. Some of the ego and astral body is left out; it has not entirely sunk down. But then it is this element that is able to perceive. Only that part of the ego and astral body perceives that has not sunk down into the etheric and physical body. When some of the astral body and ego is superfluous in such a person, then there is this inner perception, and the person can describe his or her own illness.

But now there is another condition — a condition of the opposite kind, in which the normal sleep condition is disturbed. In this case, when the ego and astral body are outside the physical and etheric body and things happen in the ego and astral body that do not belong in this soul-spiritual entity (as the things I was just describing did not belong in that physical-etheric body), when too much spirit is experienced by the ego and astral body during sleep (as too much nature was experienced in the opposite condition by the physical-etheric body), then a clairvoyance comes about that borders on a pathological state. The individual carries into sleep a certain power to perceive spiritual things, then afterward carries back memories of spiritual perception into waking consciousness. In particular, these abnormal spiritual perceptions appear in lively dreams. And then, as every initiate knows, we observe that the dreams have the following content.

Suppose the sick person, the physically sick person, is in the former condition I was describing and dips down with the spirit and soul into the physical-etheric body and then experiences the illness in a somnambulistic condition. The sick person experiences a strong catabolic process going on in the physical-etheric body, a kind of reverse process of nature. But now suppose the person is outside the physical body with the astral body and ego. Then the person has experiences of the spiritual aspect of external nature. Suppose the person experiences a sick organ inwardly — sick because it allows some outer process to occur in an unhealthy way. This is experienced in the somnambulistic state, and the inner process is described. If the person is in the opposite condition, the somnambulism works into the ego and astral body when these are farther out of the physical and etheric body. If the spiritual, elemental life of nature comes into dreams, the person experiences what is spiritual in the minerals. And what does the person dream about? The person dreams of the medicinal remedy. Here you have the connection between many aspects of somnambulistic life. The somnambulist alternates between two conditions, as I have described. In one condition dreaming of the illness, in the other condition dreaming of the remedy. And generally speaking, that is the way pathology and therapy were explored in the old mysteries.

In those times there was not so much experimenting as there is today. The sick person was brought into the temple and put into a kind of somnambulistic condition by trained temple priests. This condition was increased to the level at which the sick person could describe the process of the illness. Then the opposite somnambulistic condition was brought about, and the temple priest was told the dream that contained the therapy. This was the manner of inquiry in the oldest mysteries; it led from disease to cure. And so it was that medical science was cultivated in olden times, by seeking knowledge of humanity through the human being itself.

We don't have to go back to those old methods. We have to move forward to methods by which we are able to follow the course of an illness through imaginative experience, and by which we are able to experience the healing process through an intuitive activity that leads not into the human being, but out-ward. What has formerly been a kind of experimentation in this field will now have to become careful observation. You see the direction in which we are turning. In olden times external phys-ical science was a purely observing science; then it began to experiment and more and more substituted experiment for pure observation. That was right. But medical science did the same thing in imitation, and that was not right. It experimented on human beings with the temple research. We must find the way to change over from experimenting to observing, to an observa-tion of life that is sustained by spiritual knowledge and enriched by scientific research. For whoever really looks at life can catch a view of illness everywhere. In the simplest form of everyday life that has deviated only to the slightest degree from so-called nor-mal, something can be seen that will lead — if considered prop-erly — to a recognition of complicated disease processes. One has only to understand how things relate to one another.

But this shows us that physicians must more and more become really practical individuals — again, the exact opposite of what recent materialistic development has made them. They have gradually become pure scientists. And that makes no sense. A physician should always be able to cope with natural laws in a liv-ing way, and not just know them abstractly. With abstract knowl-edge of them one has not yet even begun to work with them. That's the situation from one side.

Let us look at the other side, the side that the priest must see. We think of the priest's mission as guiding human beings in their approach to the spiritual world, in everything that will help their ego and astral body to find their way in the spiritual world. If it is the physician's task to inquire into the nature of human-ity from a spiritual point of view, to explore pathological condi-tions from a spiritual point of view, then what must the priest look for? The priest has to find what can lead human beings toward the spiritual world; their attitude toward the spiritual world, whether they love the spiritual world, how much they are permeated by the spiritual world — insofar as these things are apparent in normal life. The priest must deal with all the normal or abnormal symptoms that the human soul manifests in this regard in everyday life. For the priest we have to point out the opposite course to that of the physician. We told the physician that if somnambulists are allowed to describe their sick organ, they will also describe the medicinal remedy for it from out of their dreams.

Let us look again at the priests in the ancient mysteries. They were not primarily interested in discovering medicinal remedies, although of course they were intensely interested in healing, for they were first and foremost a friend of humanity. But they did not stop at healing; they were interested in more than that. They were interested in the following: They saw that the somnambulist found his or her own remedy in dreams while in the spiritual world with the ego and astral body. The priests paid particular attention to this soul while it was in the spiritual world, and followed it back again into the body. And what was found? Of course they found themselves again confronting the sick organ. But now, from what they had perceived of that soul while it was out of the body, they knew how the astral body and ego would work in this organ if it were healthy. Upon returning again to the sick organ, they knew what the situation would be under healthy conditions. Now they realized how the astral body and ego out of their divine-spiritual powers take hold normally in the human organism, how they sit normally within it. The priests learned to know them in their healthy normality through the dreams in the spiritual world, and learned how they relate to the physical world when they descend into the physical body. From this, the priests learned to know the inner relation of humanity to the spiritual world.

This knowledge should influence priests as they enact the sacrament in which they are carrying back the spiritual world. For the spiritual world is present in the sacrament through the establishment of the ritual. The ritual unites spirit with physical substance by virtue of deep insight into the relation of spirit to matter. Inspirited physical substance is led back into human beings, and the relation is established in them that unites their astral body and ego within their physical and etheric bodies with the divine-spiritual being of the world. Everything in this relation depends upon the priest's celebrating the sacraments with such an attitude. Everything depends upon our permeating ourselves with such thoughts. For instance, the relation between experience in the body and experience out of the body; secrets of pathology from observing the body when it is left; secrets of therapy from observing abnormal life in the spiritual world as compared to normal perception in the spiritual world. What was established in ancient times in secret temple procedures by prominent somnambulists must now be again established by human beings developing spiritual perception in themselves and observing the connections. In this area, experiment must give way to observation.

Now it is important that the physicians and priests in the anthroposophical movement are already united in their knowledge of such facts as these. That is what really binds us together. We are permeated by a different kind of knowledge from what others have. By contrast, the idea that some sort of union or association or group should be formed is just an abstraction. What really binds us together is the possession of certain knowledge. Those who possess this knowledge obviously belong together, and should feel closely united to one another. Any external association should be an expression of the inner union created by this knowledge.

Our time suffers very much in this respect. For instance, often when I speak today to, say, a youth gathering, even though I fully appreciate their endeavor and even though I myself have the very best intentions, it is extraordinarily difficult to experience their response to the concrete truths that should be filling their souls. It is difficult when I hear them say, "The first thing we must do is to join together!" Well, indeed, everything in these last decades has been "joined together" — *ad infinitum*! People have gone on and on joining together, but they've never yet got anything real for a result by tacking zeros onto one another indefinitely —00000000 and so on. One empty consciousness to begin with, joined to another empty consciousness, joined to a third consciousness, again empty — that all adds up to nothing. By contrast, you only have to assume a content — a content that is, after all, the basis of all zeroes: one. Then you have something. It doesn't have to be a human being, but it has to be some genuine content. Interestingly enough, this assumes that there is something there to begin with. It doesn't even have to be a human being. It can be real, living knowledge. These are things we should think about in our time. For usually people are much too comfortable to search for the concrete; they are content simply to put abstractions together. Joining together is all right, of course, but it will come of itself if something concrete is there first.

Perhaps this is something that should be understood before anything else by those who work among modern humankind as physicians and priests. Today two conditions can be observed throughout the world. Generally speaking, our ego and astral body do not find properly our physical and etheric bodies, whatever our waking condition may be. Also, truly, for those observing the world as it evolves, materialistic views don't really worry them unduly! Let the monists and the others fight with one another. Nothing is accomplished thereby. But that is certainly not the fundamental evil in the evolution of humanity. If one is observing the evolutionary process, one is not particularly interested to participate in these discussions of worldviews. For actually, whether one thinks this or another thinks that, opinions are frightfully thin little things in the human soul! They're just bubbles in the reality of this world. If one bubble hits another, if one bursts, if another becomes a bit thicker from the bursting of another, none of it matters. What does matter, what should be clearly realized, is that one does not ever becomes a materialist if one is sitting with one's ego and astral body properly in the physical and etheric bodies. In other words, to be a materialist means in a finer sense to be ill. One must fill one's whole being with this knowledge. And it is not surprising in the least that when others, those who are sitting properly inside their physical and etheric bodies, encounter the sick materialists, they turn away to exactly the opposite pole — to all the vague mist of spiritualism.

Here we come to a difficult area, because these things do not take place in those parts of the world that still have a connection with one another; they happen where the world has been thrown into chaos and its pieces lie scattered about. One thing no longer reveals itself as a healing remedy for another, for they are falling away from each other. So long as sick people speak of what is going on in their organs, their dreams will still reveal the corresponding healing remedies in the outer world. But in our present time people who are ill from materialism will not be describing sick inner organs; they have broken free of their organism; they want to describe the external world, as a materialist naturally would. Then they find not remedial dreams but the opposite — false spiritualism, which is certainly not a remedy. On the contrary, it brings on the illness more strongly than ever.

And so we find today in our time — if I may draw an analogy between medical work for individuals and cultural pathology and therapy — we find that spiritualism does not by any means offer a remedy for materialism, but corresponds to the somnambulist's dream revealing his sick organs. Now sometimes a process that properly should have taken hold of a person's inner organism pushes through the organism to the periphery, to the outer world; there is then the pathological condition called a "rash." This corresponds exactly to what I've been telling you about. One sees with one's own eyes that what had been inside and is now outside is nothing healthy. It is an aberration. The physician should see clearly that materialism is a rash and needs to be regarded as a medical problem.

This will build a bridge to the priest's observation on the other side. The priest sees the symptoms that rise out of sick human souls, out of their need, out of their feelings. Spiritualism is just such a symptom. One comes to realize that in the widest sense sick life wants to sink down into the world, that all the disease in the present world outlook does indeed work itself out fully — insofar as it rests on the will — by working into people and sickening their inner life.

In the present epoch of human evolution it is impossible to see something that could be seen clearly in former times, because people in those days had different characteristics. We cannot see how a false direction of the will, a false worldview, a false view of life — all of which were designated in olden times as sin — cause illness in the organism. For they do not do so immediately in the ordinary way. We are only aware of the connection in the rarest cases, cases that are an intermediate stage between the sin and what can obviously be diagnosed as the resulting illness. These intermediate stages may simply develop into morbid conditions. But in this modern epoch the sin and the real illness are so detached from each other that now they even occur in separate incarnations. In earlier epochs they were able to appear in close connection as cause and effect, but as humanity developed they became separated so that sin appeared in one incarnation, illness in a subsequent one.

Here, then, begins the domain of the priests. Priests may no longer merely continue traditions of olden times, speaking of sin as the cause of illness. But if they have knowledge of repeated earth lives, they can speak of sin from that point of view; then they will again be speaking from the standpoint of truth. Much that priests in the world today say about these things is no longer true; it no longer corresponds to fact. These teachings originated in olden times, and today no one is interested in changing the teachings to accord with what is demanded in our time.

We have to relate ourselves to all this. Then it will be possible to make our study of pastoral medicine fruitful in both directions.

LECTURE 10

THERE IS SOMETHING THAT IS ALWAYS OVERLOOKED in this present age, something that has to do with the working, and the wanting to work, of the spiritual world. It is this: that total spiritual activity must include the creative activity to be found in human thought and feeling. What really lies at their foundation has been completely forgotten in this age of materialistic thought; today humankind is fundamentally entirely unaware of it. That is why in this very field a kind of evil mischief is perpetrated throughout our present civilization. You surely know that from every possible center, whatever it may be called, all kinds of instructions go out to people telling how they can enhance their thought power, how their thoughts can become powerful. In this way seeds are strewn in every direction of something that in earlier spiritual life was called — and still is called — "black magic." Such things are the cause of both soul illnesses and bodily illnesses, and the physician and priest must be aware of them in the course of their work. If one is alert to these things, one already has a clearer perception of the illnesses and symptoms of human soul-life. Moreover one can work to prevent them.

This is all of great importance. The intent of instruction about thought power is to give people a power they would otherwise not possess, and this is often used for pernicious reasons. There is every possible kind of instruction today with this intent — for instance, how business executives can be successful in their financial transactions. In this area a tremendous amount of mischief is perpetrated.

And what is at the bottom of it all? These things will simply become worse unless clear knowledge of them is sought precisely in the field of medicine and in the field of theology. For human thinking in recent times, particularly scientific thinking, has come enormously under the influence of materialism.

Often today people express their satisfaction over the fact that materialism in science is on the decline, that the tendency everywhere is to try to reach out beyond materialism. But truly this is slight satisfaction for those who see through these things. In the eyes of such people, the scientists or the theologians who want to overcome materialism in a modern manner are much worse than the hard-shell materialists whose assertions gradually become untenable through their very absurdity. And those who talk so glibly about spiritualism, idealism, and the like are strewing sand in people's eyes — and it's going into their own eyes as well.

For what do Driesch[13] and others do, for instance, when they want to present something that is beyond physical-material events? They use exactly the same thoughts that have been used for hundreds of years to think about the material world alone, thoughts that indeed have no other capacity than to think about the material world alone. These are the thoughts they use to think about something that is supposed to be spiritual. But such thoughts do not have that capacity. For that, one has to go to true spiritual science. That is why such strange things appear and today it is not even noticed that they are strange. A person like Driesch, for instance, recognized officially by the outer world but in reality a dilettante, holds forth to the effect that one must accept the term "psychoid." Well, if you want to ascribe to something a similarity to something else, that something else must itself be around somewhere. You can't speak of apelike creatures if there are no apes to start with. You can't speak of the "psychoid" if you say there's no such thing as a soul! And this silly nonsense is accepted today as science, honest science, science that is really striving to reach a higher level. These things must be realized. And the individuals in the anthroposophical movement who have had scientific training will be of some value in the evolution of our civilization if they don't allow themselves to be blinded by the flaring-up of will-o'-the-wisps but persist in observing carefully what is now essential to combat materialism.

Therefore the question must be asked: How is it possible for active, creative thinking to arise out of today's passive thinking? How must priests and physicians work so that creative impulses can now flow into the activity of individuals who are led and who want to be led by the spirit? Thoughts that evolve in connection with material processes leave the creative impulse outside in matter itself; the thoughts remain totally passive. That is the peculiar characteristic of our modern thought world, that the thoughts pervading the whole of science are quite passive, inactive, idle. This lack of creative power in our thinking is connected with our education, which has been completely submerged in the current passive science. Today human beings are educated in such a way that they simply are not allowed to think a creative thought — for fear that if they should actually entertain a creative thought they wouldn't be able to keep it objective but would add some subjective quirk to it! These are things that must be faced. But how can we come to creative thoughts? This can only happen if we really develop our knowledge of the human being. Humans cannot be known by uncreative thoughts, because by their very nature they themselves are creative. One must re-create if one wants knowledge. With today's passive thinking one can only understand the periphery of the human being; one has to ignore the inner being.

It is important that we really understand the place humanity has been given in this world. Today therefore, let us put something before our souls as a kind of goal that lies at the end of a long perspective, but that can make our thoughts creative — for it holds the secret for making human thought creative.

Let us think of the universe in its changing and becoming — say in the form of a circle. We may picture it like this because actually the universe as it evolves through time presents a kind of rhythmic repetition, upward and downward, with respect to many phenomena. Everywhere in the universe we find rhythms like that of day and night: other, greater rhythms that extend from one Ice Age to another, and so forth. If first we confine our inquiry to the rhythm that has the largest intervals for human perception, it will be the so-called Platonic year, which has always played an important role in human thoughts and ideas about the world when these were filled with more wisdom than they are now.

We can come to the Platonic year if we begin by observing the place where the sun rises on the first day of spring, the twenty-first of March of each year. At that moment of time the sun rises at a definite spot in the sky. We can find this spot in some constellation; attention has been given to it through all the ages, for it moves slightly from year to year. If, for instance, in 1923 we had observed this point of spring, its place in the sky in relation to the other stars, and now in 1924 observe it again, we find it is not in the same place; it lies farther back on a line that can be drawn between the constellation of Taurus and the constellation of Pisces. Every year the place where spring begins moves back in the zodiac a little bit in that direction. This means that in the course of time there is a gradual shift through all the constellations of the starry world; it can be seen and recorded. If we now inquire what the sum of all these shifts amounts to, we can see what the distance is from year to year. One year it is here, the next year there, and so on — finally it has come back to the same spot. That means after a certain period of time the place of spring's beginning must again be in the very same spot of the heavens, and for the place of its rising the sun has traveled once around the entire zodiac. When we reckon that up, it happens approximately every 25,920 years. There we have found a rhythm that contains the largest time-interval possible for a human being to perceive — the Platonic cosmic year, which stretches through approximately 25,920 of our ordinary years.

There we have looked out into the distances of the cosmos. In a certain sense we have pushed our thoughts against something from which the numbers we use bounce back. We are pushing with our thoughts against a wall. Thinking can't go any further. Clairvoyance must then come to our aid; that can go further. The whole of evolution takes place in what is encircled

by those 25,920 years. And we can very well conceive of this cir-
cumference, if you will — which obviously is not a thing of
space, but of space-time — we can conceive of it as a kind of
cosmic uterine wall. We can think of it as that which surrounds
us in farthest cosmic space.

Now let us go from what envelops us in farthest cosmic
space, from the rhythm that has the largest interval of time that
we possess, to what appears to us first of all as a small interval,
that is, the rhythm of our breathing. Now we find — again, of
course, we must use approximate numbers — we find eighteen
breaths a minute. If we reckon how many breaths a human being
takes in a day, we come to 25,920 breaths a day. We find the
same rhythm in the smallest interval, in the human being the
microcosm, as in the largest interval, the macrocosm.

Thus the human being lives in a universe whose rhythm is
the same as that of the universe itself. But only the human being,
not the animal; in just these finer details of knowledge one finally sees the difference between the human and the animal. The
essential nature of the human physical body can only be realized
if it is related to the Platonic cosmic year; 25,920 years: in that
span of time the nature of our physical body is rooted. Take a
look in *An Outline of Esoteric Science* at the tremendous time
periods, at first determined otherwise than by time and space as
we know them, through the metamorphosis of sun, moon, and
earth. Look at all the things that had to be brought together, but
not in any quantitative way; then you can begin to understand
the present human physical body with all its elements.

And now let us go to the center of the circle, where we have
the 25,920 breaths that, so to speak, place humanity in the center of the cosmic uterus. Now we have reached the ego. For in
the breathing — and remember what I said about the breathing,
that in the upper human it becomes a finer breathing for our
so-called spiritual life — we find the expression of the individual human life on earth. Here, then, we have the ego. Just as
we must grasp the connection of our physical body to the large
time interval, the Platonic cosmic year, so we must grasp the

connection of our ego — which we can feel in every breathing irregularity — to the rhythm of our breathing.

So you see, our life on earth lies between these two things — our own breathing and the cosmic year. Everything that is of any importance for the human ego is ruled by the breath. And the life of our physical body lies within those colossal processes that are ruled by the rhythm of 25,920 years. The activity that takes place in our physical body in accordance with its laws is connected with the large rhythm of the Platonic year in the same way that our ego activity is connected with the rhythm of our breathing. Human life lies in between those two rhythms. Our human life is also enclosed within physical-etheric body and astral body-ego. From a certain point of view we can say that human life on earth lies between physical body–etheric body and astral body–ego; from another point of view, from the divine, cosmic aspect, we can say human life on earth lies between a day's breathing and the Platonic year. A day's breathing is in this sense a totality; it relates to our whole human life.

But now let us consider from the cosmic standpoint what lies between human breathing, that is, the weaving life of the ego, and the course of a Platonic year, that is, the living force out in the macrocosm. As we maintain our rhythm of breathing through an entire day of twenty-four hours, we meet regularly another rhythm, the day-and-night rhythm, which is connected with how the sun stands in relation to the earth. The daily sunrise and sunset as the sun travels over the arch of heaven, the darkening of the sun by the earth, this daily circuit of the sun is what we meet with our breathing rhythm. This is what we encounter in our human day of twenty-four hours.

So let us do some more arithmetic to see how we relate to the world with our breathing, how we relate to the course of a macrocosmic day. We can figure it out in this way: Start from one day; in a year there are 360 days. (It can be approximate.) Now take a human life (again approximate) of seventy-two years, the so-called human life span. And we get 25,920 days. So we have a life of seventy-two years as the normal rhythm into which a human being is placed in this world, and we find it is the same rhythm as that of the Platonic sun year.

So our breathing rhythm is placed into our entire life in the rhythm of 25,920. One day of our life relates to the length of our entire life in the same rhythm as one of our breaths relates to the total number of our breaths during one day. What is it, then, that appears within the seventy-two years, the 25,920 days in the same way that a breath, one inhalation-exhalation, appears within the whole breathing process? What do we find there? First of all we have inbreathing-outbreathing, the first form of the rhythm. Second, as we live our normal human life there is something that we experience 25,920 times. What is that? Sleeping and waking. Sleeping and waking are repeated 25,920 times in the course of a human life, just as inbreathing and out-breathing are repeated 25,920 times in the course of a human day. But now we must ask, what is this rhythm of sleeping and waking? Every time we go to sleep we not only breathe carbon dioxide out, but as physical human beings we breathe our astral body and ego out. When we wake, we breathe them in again. That is a longer inbreathing-outbreathing: it takes twenty-four hours, a whole day. That is a second form of breathing that has the same rhythm. So we have a small breath, our ordinary inhalation-exhalation; and we have a larger breath by which we go out into the world and back, the breath of sleeping-waking.

But let us go further. Let us see how the average human life of seventy-two years fits into the Platonic cosmic year. Let us count the seventy-two years as belonging to one great year, a year consisting of days that are human lives. Let us reckon this great cosmic year in which each single day is a whole human life. Then count the cosmic year also as having 360 days, which would mean 360 human lives. Then we would get 360 human lives x 72 years = 25,920 years: the Platonic year.

What does this figure show us? We begin a life and die. What do we do when we die? When we die, we breathe out more than our astral body and ego from our earthly organism. We also breathe our etheric body out into the universe. I have

often indicated how the etheric body is breathed out, spread out
into the universe. When we come back to earth again, we
breathe our etheric body in again. That is a giant breath. An
etheric inbreathing-outbreathing. Mornings we breathe in the
astral element, while with our physical breath we breathe in oxygen. With each earth-death we breathe the etheric element out;
with each earth-life we breathe the etheric element in.

So there we have the third form of breathing: life and
death. If we count life to be our life on earth, and death to be our
life between death and a new birth, then we have the largest
form of breathing in the cosmic year:

    1. Inhalation-exhalation, the smallest breath.
    2. Sleeping-waking, a larger breath.
    3. Life-death, the largest breath.

Thus we stand first and foremost in the world of the stars.
Inwardly, we relate to our ordinary breathing; outwardly, we
relate to the Platonic year. In between, we live our human life,
and exactly the same rhythm is revealed in this human life itself.

But what comes into this space between the Platonic year
and our breathing rhythm? Like a painter who prepares a can-
vas and then paints on it, let us try painting on the base we have
prepared, that is, the rhythms we have found in numbers.
With the Platonic year as with smaller time rhythms, especially with the rhythm of the year, we find that continual change
goes on in the outer world. Also it is change that we perceive;
we perceive it most easily in temperatures: warmth and cold.
We need only to think of cold winter and warm summer —
here again we could present numbers, but let us take the qualitative aspect of warmth and cold. Human beings live life within this alternation between warmth and cold. In the outer world
the alternation is within the element of time; and for so-called
nature, changing in a time sequence from one to the other is
quite healthful. But human beings cannot do this. We have, in
a certain sense, to maintain a normal warmth — or a normal

coldness, if you will — within ourselves. We have to develop inner forces by which we save some summer warmth for winter and some winter cold for summer. In other words, we must keep a proper balance within; we must be so continually active in our organism that it maintains a balance between warmth and cold no matter what is happening outside.

There are activities within the human organism of which we are quite unaware. We carry summer within us in winter and winter within us in summer. When it is summer, we carry within us what our organism experienced in the previous winter. We carry winter within us through the beginning of spring until St. John's Day; then the change comes. As autumn approaches, we begin to carry the summer within us, and we keep it until Christmas, until December 21, when the balance shifts again. So we carry in us this continual alternation of warmth and cold. But what are we doing in all this?

When we examine what we are doing, we find something extraordinarily interesting. Let this be the human being (see drawing below).

We realize from simple superficial observation that everything that enters the human being as cold shows the tendency to go to the nerve-sense system. And today we can point out that

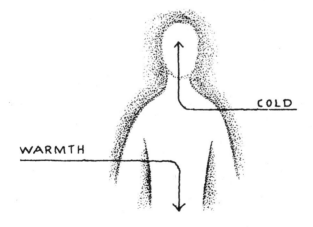

everything that works as cold, everything of a winter nature, works in the building up of our head, of our nerve-sense organization. Everything of a summer nature, everything that contains warmth, is given over to our metabolic-limb system. If we look at our metabolic-limb system, we can see that we carry within it everything summery. If we look at our nerve-sense functions, we can see that we carry in them everything we receive out of the universe that is wintry. So in our head we always have winter; in our metabolic-limb system we always have summer. And our rhythmic system maintains the balance between the one and the other. Warmth-cold, warmth-cold, metabolic system–head system, with a third system keeping them in balance. Material warmth is only a result of warmth processes, and material cold the result of cold processes. So we find a play of cosmic rhythm in the human organism. We can say that winter in the macrocosm is the creative force in the human nerve-sense system centered in the head. Summer in the macrocosm is the creative force in the human metabolic-limb system.

This way of looking into the human organism is another example of the initiatic medicine of which I spoke when I said it has a beginning in the book[14] that Dr. Wegman worked out with me. The beginning is there for what must more and more become a part of science.

If we climb the rocks where the soil is so constituted that winter plants will grow in it, we come to that part of the outer world that is related to the organization of the human head. Let us suppose that we collect medicinal substances out in the world. We want to make sure that the spiritual forces appearing in an illness that originates in the nerve-sense system will be healed by the spirit in outer nature, so we climb very high in the mountains to find minerals and plants and bring them down for medicines for head illnesses. We are acting out of our creative thinking. It starts our legs moving toward things we must find in the earth that correspond to our medical needs. The right thoughts — and they come out of the cosmos — must impel us all the way to concrete deeds. These thoughts can stir us without our knowledge. People, say, who work in an office — they also have thoughts, at least they sometimes have them — now they are impelled by some instinct to go off on all sorts of hikes. Only they don't know the real reason — but that doesn't matter. It only becomes important if one observes such people from a physician's or a priest's standpoint. But a true view of the world also gives one inspiration for what one has to do in detail.

Now again, if we have to do with illnesses in the metabolic-limb system, we look for low-growing plants and for minerals in the soil. We look for what occurs as sediment, not for what grows above the earth in crystal form. Then we get the kind of mineral and plant remedies we need. That is how observation of the connection between processes in the macrocosm and processes in man lead one from pathology to therapy.

These connections must again be clearly understood. In olden times people knew them well. Hippocrates was really a latecomer as far as ancient medicine is concerned. But if you read a little of what he is supposed to have written, of what at any rate still preserved his spirit, you will find this viewpoint throughout. All through his writings you will find that the concrete details relate to broad knowledge and observation such as we have been presenting. In later times, such things were no longer of any interest. People came more and more to mere abstract, intellectual thinking and to an external observation of nature that led to mere experimentation. We must find the way back again to what was once vision of the relation between the human being and the world.

We live as human beings on the earth between our ego and our physical body, between breathing and the Platonic year. With our breathing we have a direct relation to the day. What do we relate to with our physical body? How do we relate physically to the Platonic year? There we relate to totally external conditions in the evolution of large natural processes — for instance, to climatic changes. In the course of the large natural processes human beings change their form, so that, for instance, successive racial forms appear, and so forth. We relate qualitatively to what happens in the shorter external changes, to what successive years and days bring us. In short, we evolve as human beings between these two farthest boundaries. But in between we can be free, because in between, even in the macrocosm, a remarkable element intervenes.

One can be lost in wonder in pondering over this rhythm of 25,920 years. One is awed by what happens between the universe and the human being. And as one contemplates all this, one realizes that the whole world — including the human being — is ordered according to measure, number, and weight. Everything is wonderfully ordered — but it all happens to be human calculation! And at important moments when we are explaining a calculation — even though it is correct — we always have to add that curious word "approximately." For our human calculation never comes out exactly right. It is all absolutely logical; order and reason are in everything, they are alive and active, everything "works," as we say. And yet there is something in all of it, something in the universe that is completely irrational. Something is there so that however profound our awe may be, even as initiates, when we go for an afternoon walk we still take an umbrella along. We take an umbrella because something could happen that is irrational. Something can appear in the life of the universe that simply "doesn't come out right" when numbers are applied to it. And so one has had to invent leap years, intercalary months, all kinds of things. Such things have always had to be used for the fixing of time. What is offered by a well-developed astronomy that has deepened into astrology and astrosophy (for one can think of it in that way) is all destroyed for immediate use by meteorology. This latter has not attained the rank of a rational science; it is more or less permeated by vision, and will be, more and more. It takes an entirely different path; it consists of what is left over by the other sciences. Modern astronomy itself lives only in names; it is really nothing more than a system for giving names to stars. That is why even Serenissimus came to the end of his knowledge when newly found stars had to have names. He would visit the observatories in his country and let them show him various stars through the telescope, then after seeing everything he would say, "Yes, I know all that — but how you know what that star's name is, that very distant star, that's what I don't understand." Yes, of course it's obvious, the standpoint you've adopted at this moment when you laugh at Serenissimus. But there's another standpoint: one could laugh at the astronomers. I'd rather you'd laugh at the astronomers, because there's something very strange going on in the world as it evolves.

If you want to inquire into the old way of naming things, Saturn and so forth, you should think back to our speech course,[15] and recall that in olden times names were given from the feeling the astrologers and astrosophers had for the sound of some particular star. All the old star names were God-given, spirit-given. The stars were asked what their names were, because the tone of the star was always perceived and its name was then given accordingly. Now, indeed, you come to a certain boundary line in the development of astrosophy and astrology. Earlier they had to get the names from heaven. When you come to more recent times when the great discoveries were made, for instance, of the "little fellows" (*Sternwichten*), then everything is mixed up. One is called Andromeda, another has another Greek name. Everything is mixed up in high-handed fashion. One can't think that Neptune and Uranus are as truly characterized by their names as Saturn was. Now there is only human arbitrariness. And Serenissimus made one mistake. He believed the astronomers were carrying on their work similarly to the ancient astrosophers. But this was not so. They possessed only a narrow human knowledge, while the knowledge of the astrosophers of olden times, and astrologers of still older times, came directly out of humanity's intercourse with the gods. However, if today one would return from astronomy to astrology or astrosophy, and thereby have a macrocosm to live in that is rational throughout, then one would reach Sophia. Then one would find too that within this rationality and Sophia-wisdom meteoronomy, meteorology, and meteorosophy are the things that "don't come out right" by our human calculation, and one can only question them at their pleasure! That's another variety of Lady! In ordinary everyday life, one calls a lady capricious. And the meteorological Lady is capricious all the way from rainshowers to comets. But as one gradually advances from meteorology to meteorosophy one discovers the finer attributes of this world queen, attributes that do not come merely from caprice or cosmic emotion, but from the Lady's warm heart. But nothing will be accomplished unless in contrast to all the arithmetic, all the thinking, all that can be calculated rationally one acquires a direct acquaintance with the beings of the cosmos and learns to know them as they are. They are there; they do show themselves — shyly perhaps at first, for they are not obtrusive. With calculations one can go further and further, but then one is getting further and further away from the true nature of the world. For one is only reaching deeds from the past.

If one advances from ordinary calculation to the calculating of rhythms as it was in astrology for the harmony of the spheres, one goes on from the calculating of rhythms to a view of the organization of the world in numbers, as we find them in astrosophy. On the other hand one finds that the ruling world beings are rather shy. They do not appear at once. First they only present a kind of Akasha photography, and one is not sure of its source. One has the whole world to look at, but only in photographs displayed in various parts of the cosmic ether. And one does not know where they come from.

Then inspiration begins. Beings come out of the pictures and make themselves known. We move out of "-nomy" — but just to "-logy." Only when we push through all the way to intuition does the being itself follow from inspiration and we come to Sophia. But this is a path of personal development that requires the effort of the whole human being. The whole human being must become acquainted with such a Lady, who hides behind meteorology — in wind and weather, moon and sun insofar as they intervene in the elements. Not just the head can be engaged as in "-logy," but the whole human being is needed.

Already there is a possibility of taking the wrong path in this endeavor. You can even come to Anthroposophy through the head — by coming from anthroponomy, which is today the supreme ruling science, to anthropology. There you just have rationality, nothing more. But rationality is not alive. It describes only the traces, the footprints, of life and it gives one no impulse to investigate details. Yet life really consists of details and of the irrational element. What your head has grasped, you have to take down into the whole human being, and then with the whole human being progress from "-nomy" to "-logy," finally to "-sophy," which is Sophia.

We must have a feeling for all this if we want to enliven theology on the one side and medicine on the other through what can truly enliven them both — pastoral medicine. But the essential thing is that first of all, at the very outset of our approach to pastoral medicine, we learn to know the direction it should take in its observation of the world.

LECTURE 11

PASTORAL MEDICINE AS WE THINK OF IT HERE will only be recognized as something from spiritual research that has meaning when humankind once more possesses a common consciousness of a spiritual realm containing positive, active forces. For naturally in an age that has developed materialism, it is inconceivable to the ordinary human being that anyone could have seen something worthy of notice in the spiritual world. But this really happened in the old mysteries. Individuals saw into spiritual realms and found knowledge there that led to valuable cures. And what we still have to say today to round off our studies may perhaps provide a connection to that old mystery wisdom for the medical stream that should now emanate from the Goetheanum.

Indeed this impulse is understood most correctly in its historical connection if what is intended here is thought of as having developed out of the research methods (although, of course, quite different in form) and the artistic healing practices of the old mysteries. Obviously you will have to regard what has been offered in this short course as just a stimulus, as in a certain sense just the first chapter, the beginning of a pastoral medicine that will develop further through the work that is still to be done here by Dr. Wegman and me.

So first I would like to point out how the initiates in the old mysteries described their path of initiation, particularly that path that was pursued at the place where the mysteries were most involved in the secrets of healing. Actually all the mysteries were connected with secrets of healing, but some more than others. They were all connected with them because healing was regarded as related to the entire evolution of human civilization. There were deep reasons for this. People of those ancient times said: When the human being comes down out of spiritual worlds into the physical-earth world through conception and birth, the soul-spiritual entity undergoes a transformation by which it is able to form a physical human body. We have described how this achievement takes place for the first time through the activity of the individual during the first seven years of life. The first body had been given through heredity, the body that in the course of the first seven or eight years is entirely stripped off.

Thus it was conceived very exactly in the ancient mysteries how one came out of spiritual worlds into the world of the physical senses. But there was a universal recognition that a person does not in the first place unite with the physical body in the way that was originally intended by the spiritual powers who direct humanity. It was always believed that through some anomaly of the general evolution the forces that a human being inherits overpower in a certain sense the forces that are brought through the individuality from former earth-lives. This seemed to show a lack of harmony. It was said: If there were complete harmony between soul-and-spirit and physical body in earthly humans, death would not have the form it now has; nor would illness come in the way it now comes. Illness and death were regarded as the symptoms that show that human beings indeed have more to do with the physical-earth world than they were originally meant to. Although today this can no longer be completely understood, still it is an extremely profound idea in which there is very much truth. For the moment one reaches a higher level of consciousness even to a slight degree, one sees at once that death is quite different in character. It appears as a metamorphosis rather than the end of a phase of life.

Therefore for the entire ancient consciousness the education of the human being was related to healing. The entire educational process in very ancient times of human evolution was thought of primarily from a medical point of view. Connected with this was the recognition that the mysteries united the professions of physician and priest, both of whom should be concerned with the healing of human beings on earth. Usually in olden times physician and priest were united in one person. This could only happen out of the old instinctive consciousness; today it would not be possible, at least not as an accepted custom. This recognition of the importance of healing, which was strong even in normally healthy persons, was related for every human being to their knowledge that after the metamorphosis they would undergo through death, they would be guided through their life between death and rebirth on their path to the sun by souls who on earth had been physicians or priests. The first need of every human being after death was to find the sun path — because there they would work out part of what they had to experience between death and rebirth. And these first steps had to be shown to them by a physician or a priest. So it was thought in ancient times. This was included in the deepest mystery wisdom. For us today this wisdom must be regarded differently because the old methods are no longer suitable for us. However, at this present time they can be renewed. Indeed that renewal is to be attempted right here.

When ancient initiates described their initiation they would say that after they had crossed the threshold they were first made acquainted with the activity of the elements. In olden times, "elements" was the name given to what today would be called physical conditions. That is, the solid, which was called "earth"; all fluids, which were called "water"; everything gaseous, which was called "air"; and everything to do with "warmth," which was ascribed to the warmth ether and which was called an element. Modern physicists deny all this. For them these four elements do not exist. For them there are from sixty to eighty elements, which have qualities. Under certain conditions one is fluid, another solid or gaseous. The condition of warmth belongs to all. What was described as an element in olden times does not exist today. There are now only qualities of things; the qualities have no existence of their own. What today are called elements are actually only "real" in the coarse, tangible physical world. And what in olden times were called elements were understood not as reaching down into tangible matter itself, but only to the intangible, living activity of matter.

It was of no particular importance to an ancient physician whether something was this or that substance with this or that name. Naturally this is important, but it only becomes so after one has first obtained full view of something else, of the living, weaving activity of the substance. Thus one can study a substance in a place where it is exposed to weather conditions. The ancient physicians laid great value on studying a substance while it was being exposed to the weather, to the whole earth process. Also they took care that they did not simply take some substance out of the mineral kingdom if it could be obtained from the plant kingdom. In other words, they looked at the position the substance had in the world process by virtue of its living activity. But to understand that, one needs to accept the concept of the four elements. For then it is of prime importance in what temperature a substance becomes earth, for instance; in what temperature it becomes solid, or fluid, or air. That was the important thing in olden times, to observe what world process must happen so that some substance or other would take on a particular form. That was the first requirement. After that, the substance was examined without restriction. Today one starts out from the substance; formerly one started out from the process. And in fact any substance is only a process suspended at a certain stage. Formerly people were above all concerned with the whole weaving life within the material substance. And so initiates described how they were led to a vision of the weaving life of matter and of how it appeared to them as a fabric woven of the four elements. That was the first experience.

The second description everyone gave, which presented the second step for them, was this: they were led to a place where they could learn to know the "upper and lower gods." What does that mean? We have already described that, but in a modern way. I told you that if the soul-spiritual entity enters too deeply into the physical and etheric bodies, these bodies overpower the soul-spiritual entity, creating a pathological condition — an aberration of the soul-spiritual entity in the physical-etheric organism. There is, then, this pathological situation, that such people have descended more deeply into the physical organism than they should in ordinary waking life, and down below encounter non-human, subnatural activity. For only when we have a normal relation between our soul and spirit and our physical-etheric organism do we live in the natural world. The moment we descend too deeply, too intensely into physical corporeality, we come into relation with the subnatural. We fall to a level at which elemental beings, beings of higher hierarchies at various stages of their development, are all active. We come into relation with those gods who are unfolding their activity below the level of nature.

How would ancient initiates have spoken if they had wanted to use a more neutral expression, veiling the facts so that no one would understand them except other initiates? How could they have implied that they had been led to the lower gods? An ancient initiate would have said: I have learned to know the nature of human illnesses. For that leads to the lower gods.

Now look in the other direction, at the life of the saint: this also, as I have shown you, can be at the borderline between normal and pathological. It can happen that the soul-spiritual entity goes out farther than it should, enhancing the sleep condition. The ancient initiates described their introduction to this state as meeting with the upper gods. Put schematically (see drawing), this corresponds to the facts: nature, subnature, super-

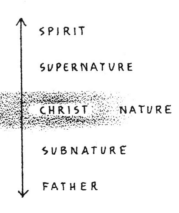

SPIRIT

SUPERNATURE

CHRIST   NATURE

SUBNATURE

FATHER

nature. Visionary life, through the clairvoyant faculty that leads
an individual into the spiritual world: the initiate called this
"meeting with the upper gods."

Now when we speak of upper and lower gods someone can
very easily entertain the false idea that it concerns rank. You
must think of it in this way: if I simply say nature, subnature,
supernature, illness, visionary life, then I am tempted to think of
the lower gods as being of a lower order. But that is not true. In
reality it is like the drawing below.

Imagine we have nature; then above, it leads to a circle;
below, it leads to a circle; and what is above joins what is below.
If we draw the circle larger and larger, and continue to draw it
larger, we finally get a straight line. A piece of circle that continues on, after it has gone into infinity, comes back from the other side. This shows that the terms "upper" and "lower" are not to
be understood as signs of rank, but simply as different ways that
the gods come to human beings. They have been thought of as
working in equal rank with one another, of striving to unite at a
point in infinity. Therefore everything in olden times that was
either illness or clairvoyance was thought to show that those

who gained an understanding of those two human conditions, would then see into the spiritual world. One way to know about the spiritual world was to become well acquainted with illness and with clairvoyance. When we understand this, we are able to bring into our own modern age what was present in human consciousness in olden times. If we ask what can be identified in modern consciousness with the realm of the lower gods, the answer must be — the Being whom we call the Father when we think of the divine Trinity. The Father belongs in the most eminent sense to subnature. How are we to think about the Father God with truly spiritual comprehension?

Let us consider human beings, first in day-waking consciousness, then in night-sleeping consciousness, and let us compare the two states. We know that in full waking consciousness individuals are living as they have been placed to live within the order of this physical world. Just as the earth has had earlier stages of evolution — Saturn, Sun, Moon — and will undergo further evolution, so must humans themselves be recognized as the result of those earlier evolutionary periods. In this sense they belong in their waking state to the earth; by their nature they stand within the sphere of the earth. In waking condition they stand on a level with nature.

It is not the same when human beings sleep. When we are asleep our physical and etheric bodies lie on the bed, and our astral body and ego are outside them. Let us look at the physical and etheric bodies. Of what do we consist, lying there in our physical and etheric bodies? We have — of course, at a more advanced stage — what we received in the old Saturn evolution and the old Sun evolution. That is now further evolved; we have the further development of our Saturn and Sun existence now during sleep. We do not have our Moon existence in what lies there on the bed. Nature has progressed from Moon existence to Earth existence. And the fact that the sleep condition is essential to us means that nature preserves in the sleeping human being a nature that is now below, a nature that only existed during the Saturn and Sun periods. That is subnature. That lies at the foundation of all beings through the fact that there is a human race. Humans fall during sleep into subnature, and from this fall illnesses appear. That is the realm of the Father God. When we sleep we enter the realm of the Father God, we enter subnature, the realm of the Father.

Human clairvoyance helps illuminate the members of the human being that during sleep are outside the physical and etheric bodies: that is, the ego and astral body. When we become conscious in them, we are in the opposite condition, the opposite pole to illness and have entered the realm of the Spirit with the astral body and ego.

So we can see that the human being is organized on earth in such a way that one is able to go out from nature in two directions, in the direction of subnature to the Father, and in the direction of supernature to the Spirit. Since the Mystery of Golgotha, Christ has been the mediator for both worlds. He is the one who permeates the world of nature, the one who permeates normal human existence. He has always to create harmony between subnature and supernature. Subnature is always kept in balance by the normal course of sleeping and waking. Supernature is kept in balance by those seers who are able to return to their ordinary human life at will. If someone is unable upon waking from sleep to balance what is experienced in subnature, then there is illness in the physical and etheric bodies. If someone is unable to bring back into the full waking state, into the natural course of earth-life, what is experienced clairvoyantly in the realm of the spirit, then there are soul illnesses or spiritual illnesses. This is the other pole.

Let us now consider physical illness. What happens when the healing process starts? The human being is led from the experience of subnature to the experience of nature, from the Father to Christ. For Christ is the spiritual life in nature. That is in reality what the physician does. It is the physician's task to know how a person fallen to subnature is brought back to Christ, after the Father has given the leadership over to Christ the Son. That puts into modern speech what mystery wisdom would express. After initiates have attained a Christ-consciousness here on earth, they are led on the one side to the Father, on the other side to the Spirit. If then they are aware how their path leads from the Father to Christ, they will find all the healing processes on this path.

Here the modern mystery begins, the mystery that creates a great test for real medical science. It is this to which I must point at the conclusion of this pastoral medicine course, so that there shall flow from it what should first of all bestow healing upon physicians. We can assume that they will gradually learn the separate healing measures that we have shown in this course by learning which are the defective organs and then what in outer nature corresponds to them and will work with spiritual power. Thus we introduce spirit as the healing agent into the human body. The physicians will learn how it is done in a given case. This will all build up for them into a complete knowledge. This living knowledge that they attain will be different from the current conventional knowledge. If today you open your pathology text or a medical textbook and study it thoroughly, at the end you are no further along than you were at the beginning. Granted, you have digested the entire contents, but even while you worked at it chapter after chapter, still you were making no progress in your general human attitude. It is the nature of real knowledge that it impels one to grow in one's entire human attitude.

If you take up medicine in this sense and as it was meant in this pastoral medicine course, you will advance step by step. And the result will be nothing less than that you can say to yourselves: Now that I have my medical training behind me, I understand all that transpired at the Mystery of Golgotha, up to the moment when Christ went through the gate of death. You will understand the passage of Christ from the Father to the death on Golgotha. That is the mystery. One may not believe at first that medicine is related to this mystery, but it is. It is so truly related that through your understanding of the processes of healing, you will grasp what happened in the cosmos when the Father sent the Son to undergo the death on Golgotha. You will see in the death on Golgotha not death but the working together of all that happened at the death. That was not a death but the overcoming of death and the healing of all mankind. That is the path of the physician, from Father to Son until the Son dies on Golgotha. All separate pieces of medical knowledge bring one a step further toward the final comprehension of this Mystery.

Pastoral medicine is not only what the pastor and the physician are to practice together, it is what is to be brought together so that first through the physician one part of the Mystery of Golgotha can be really understood. That is the high point, the ultimate achievement of medicine: to comprehend all human illness in such a way that one sees the Mystery of Golgotha up to the death as a tremendous healing process. The pathology of evolving humanity and the therapy, the dying on the cross — these will be seen in their true connection when we have real medicine.

The priest has to follow all that is experienced by human beings when they leave their body and enter the other world, the world of the spirit. Thereby priests become more and more aware of the relation of a human being to the Spirit, to the *spiritus sanctus*, the Holy Spirit. And their path is that of mediation between the Spirit and the Son, the Christ, of developing theology so it will find the way from Christ to the Spirit, from the Spirit to Christ. A great sum of knowledge and life experience can be acquired on this path along which one has to lead one's fellow humans from the Spirit to Christ, from Christ to the Spirit. Its highest service must be that the successive stages of theology are able to clarify the meaning of Christ's path after the death on Golgotha. For his going through the death on Golgotha was the great healing event. Then the question arises: what faculty does this healing event create in human beings that will help them to enter the spiritual world? Theology must have for its crowning endeavor the comprehension of what is happening to the Christ individuality since He went through the death on Golgotha.

Christ's path to Golgotha: the peak of the physician's path.
Christ's path after Golgotha: the peak of the priest's path.

For many contemporary theologians, the two paths seem to have no connection whatever. There are theologians today who do not want to know anything about the risen Spirit and the further activity of the Christ. But if we speak in the sense of a renewal of the mysteries, then the event of Golgotha, the Mystery of Golgotha belongs to it. And then we can say that the path by which the ancient initiate came to initiation could be described in this way: I was led through the elements to the lower and higher gods. The modern initiate would describe it as follows: I have been led through what dissolves the elements into their active processes — the elements are now the chemical elements, eighty of them, that dissolve when they enter into any process — and I am led further, to the Father below and the Spirit above. I perceive the activity of Christ on both paths.

If you would like to take a summary of this course with you for your esoteric study, then take these words:

I will follow the path
That dissolves the elements into activity,
And leads me down to the Father
Who sends illness to work out karma,
And leads me up to the Spirit
Who guides the erring soul toward freedom.
The Christ leads downward and upward,
Creating Spirit-Man in earth humanity
In harmonious union.

Ich werde gehen den Weg,
Der die Elemente in Geschehen löst
Und mich führt nach unten zum Vater
Der die Krankheit schickt zum Ausgleich des Karma
Und mich führt nach oben zum Geiste

Der die Seele in Irrtum zum Erwerb der Freiheit leitet
Christus führt nach unten und nach oben
Harmonisch Geistesmensch in Erdenmenschen zeugend.

When you have become completely permeated by the content of this brief meditation, you will have taken livingly into your spirit what I wanted to give in this course.

Notes

1. Cesare Lombroso (1836–1909), Italian anthropologist. Wrote *Genius and Insanity* (1864) and *The Criminal: Anthropological, Medical and Legal Aspects* (1876).

2. Rudolf Steiner, *An Outline of Esoteric Science* (Hudson, N.Y.: Anthroposophic Press, 1985).

3. *Pythians:* priestesses of Apollo who delivered the oracles at Delphi.

4. Teresa of Avila (1515–1582), Carmelite nun. Reformed the Carmelite Order in association with John of the Cross. Canonized by the Catholic Church.

5. Mechthild von Magdeburg (1210–1286?). Cistercian nun. Her chief work was *The Flowing Light of the Godhead.*

6. Kali Yuga, "the Dark Age," reckoned from 3101 B.C. to A.D. 1899 in Steiner's esoteric chronology.

7. Ferdinand Raimund (1790–1836). Viennese dramatist. Wrote *Der Alpenkönig und der Menschenfeind* ("King of the Alps and the Misanthrope," 1828).

8. Wilhelm Preyer (1811–1897). Professor of Physiology. Wrote *Hypotheses Concerning the Origin of Life in Scientific Facts and Problems* (1880).

9. Rudolf Steiner, *Autobiography* (Hudson, N.Y.: Anthroposophic Press, 1999).

10. Johannes Müller (1801–1858). Berlin physiologist.

11. Paracelsus (1493–1541). Swiss physician and alchemist.

12. *"The sickest entity..."* This refers to a European expression, "the sick man of Europe," applied to the Ottoman Empire in the nineteenth century.

13. Hans Driesch (1867–1941). Scientist and philosopher.

14. Rudolf Steiner and Ita Wegman, *Extending Practical Medicine* (London: Rudolf Steiner Press, 1996).

15. Rudolf Steiner, *Speech and Drama* (Hudson, N.Y.: Anthroposophic Press, 1986).

INDEX

A

abdominal organs, 37
active meditation, 35
active prayer, 35
adrenal glands, 32
air, 96, 98, 101, 149
Alexander, 62
alien elemental, 96
angel, 49–50
anointing, 20
anthropology, 145
anthroponomy, 145
Anthroposophical physician,
    18–19
Anthroposophy, 92, 145
    bringing theologians and
        physicians together, 17
    encountering insane, 31
    knowledge used in
        understanding spiritual
        experiences, 41
    physical and spiritual
        working together, 25
    picture of man from, 28
antimony, 47
    anxiety, relation to breathing
        irregularities, 86–87
anxiety elementals, 86–87
Aquinas, Thomas, 15
arterial circulation, 103
arterial process, 104
Artistotle, 62
asceticism, 20

astral body, 9, 10, 29
    approaching etheric body,
        14, 109
    breathing as activity of,
        96–97
    coarseness of, 37
    consistency of, 37
    in death, 14
    in disturbed sleep, 123
    drawing ego down, 67–71
    in initiation, 14
    knowledge of, 11
    living in, 109
    not finding physical and
        etheric bodies, 128
    physical body a true image
        of, 28
    role in insanity, 31, 32
    role in mental retardation,
        10
    second stage of
        development, 28
    in sleep, 97, 119, 120, 153
    in sleepwalking, 123, 124
    uniting with divine-spiritual
        being, 127
astral body–ego, 136
astral forces, 59
astrology, 142, 143
astronomy, 142, 143
astrosophy, 142, 143, 144
Atlantean time, 94–95
automatic speech, cause of, 78

Movement for Religious
Renewal, 25
Müller, Johannes, 103
musical forms, 28–29

N

naming, 143
natural science, 93–95
nature, 152
nature-spirit balance, 50–51
neighbor, love of, 32
Neptune, 143
nerve-sense-arterial process,
104
nerve-sense inhalation, 103
nerve-sense process, 102
nerve-sense system, 43, 85, 98,
139–40
nervous system, 43
non-ego, 121
nonrenewal, bodily, 61

O

obesity, in children, 64
O'Connor, Flannery, 12
occult forces, resting in, 75
offering, flame of, 18
opinions, 128
order, 142
organs
excessive astrality in, 72–73
living in, 110
Outline of Esoteric Science, An
(Steiner), 10, 28, 135
oxygen, 86, 96

P–Q

pain
source of, 44
transformed into bliss,
40–41, 44
Paracelsus, 108
parallel experiences of
consciousness, 41, 42
paranoia, 75
parents, resemblance to, 55
passive meditation, 35–36
passive prayer, 35–36
passive science, 133
pastoral medicine
course for, 19–20, 25–26
determining direction, 145
embracing working
together, 117
hygienics of, 20
loss of original meaning, 17
preventative role of, 73
recognition of, 147
understanding mystery of
Golgotha, 156
Pastoral Medicine, 8
pathological, categorization of,
27
pathological condition, healthy
counterparts to, 46–47
pathology
karmic influence on, 89–90
from overpowering soul-
spiritual entity, 150–51
resulting from astral body
drawing ego down, 70
pedagogy, 77
perception, threshold of, stages
of, 39

THE FOUNDATIONS OF
ANTHROPOSOPHICAL MEDICINE
LECTURES AND WRITINGS BY RUDOLF STEINER

In response to requests from doctors and medical students, Rudolf Steiner gave the first lectures outlining an "anthroposophically extended medicine" in March, 1920—anticipating by more than sixty years the essentially postmodern idea of integrative or complementary medicine. Originally scheduled for two weeks, the initial meeting was lengthened to three, so that physicians could also make presentations on their own work. Anthroposophical medicine thus grows out of the realities of medical *practice*.

Steiner, by training a scientist and a Goetheanist, had always been interested in medicine and the art of healing. At different periods of his life, he had lectured and written on medical subjects and advised physicians on their work. He could do this because, besides being thoroughly versed in contemporary medical methods, he had worked through and understood the bases of traditional Western medicine exemplified by the alchemical tradition that runs from Paracelsus through Van Helmont to Hahnemann, the creator of homeopathy—the traditional medicine of the West.

This Paracelsian, alchemical tradition was close to his heart and to the heart of anthroposophy, the new science of the spirit. For this reason, together with his close associate Dr. Ita Wegman, Steiner actively encouraged the development of anthroposophically extended medicine, which now enjoys a growing worldwide reputation both for its methodology and for specific treatments such as Iscador (mistletoe) for cancer.

Throughout the four years remaining to him, Steiner continued to lecture once or twice a year to physicians and consult with those undertaking to incorporate these new ideas into their clinical practice. At the same time, clinics were created and a training program instituted. The Foundations of Anthroposophical Medicine series will include all of Steiner's medical lectures and writings.

(Titles as given are translations of the German titles as they appear in the Collected Works (GA). The titles as published in English may vary.)

1. **Spiritual Science and Medicine: First Medical Course** (Twenty Lectures, Dornach, March 21–April 9, 1920). *Geisteswissenschaft und Medizin* GA 312. Published as *Introducing Anthroposophical Medicine* (1999)

2. **Spiritual Scientific Perspectives on Therapy: Second Medical Course** (Nine Lectures, Dornach, April 11–April 18, 1921). *Geisteswissenschaftliche Gesichtspunkte zur Therapie* GA 313

3. **Physiology and Therapy on the Basis of Spiritual Science** (Four Lectures, Dornach, October 7–October 9, 1920); **Anthroposophical Foundations for an Art of Remedies** (Four Lectures, Stuttgart, October 26–28, 1922); **On Therapy** (Three Lectures, Dornach, December 31, 1923–January 2, 1924); **Miscellaneous discussions, etc.** *Physiologisch-Therapeutisches auf Grundlage der Geisteswissenschaft. Zur Therapie und Hygiene* GA 314

4. **Curative Eurythmy** (Seven Lectures, Dornach, April 12–April 18, 1921; One Lecture, Stuttgart, October 28, 1922). *Heileurythmie* GA 315

5. **Meditative Considerations and Directions for Deepening the Art of Healing.** *Meditative Betrachtungen und Anleitungen zur Vertiefung der Heilkunst* GA 316

6. **Curative Education** (Twelve Lectures, Dornach, June 25–July 12, 1924). *Heilpädadagogischer Kurs* GA 317

7. **Broken Vessels** (Eleven Lectures, Dornach, September 8–September 18, 1924). *Pastoral-Medizinischer Kurs* GA 318

8. **Medicine and the Anthroposophical View of the Human Being** (Eleven Lectures, various cities, 1923/24). *Anthroposophische Menschenerkenntnis und Medizin* GA 319. *Published as The Healing Process: Spirit, Nature & Our Bodies* (2000).

9. **Miscellaneous Lectures on Spiritual Science and Medicine I**

10. **Miscellaneous Lectures on Spiritual Science and Medicine II**

11. **Extending Medicine on the Basis of Spiritual Science** (Fundamentals of Therapy). Steiner and Wegman. *Grundlegendes für eine Erweiterung der Heilkunst nach geisteswissenschaftlichen Erkenntnissen* GA 27